RENOVATION
MANAGEMENT
COMPANY

# THE
# W
# RE          OR

## A Home                        aging
## Contract                       tions

*Save time, r                     rriage...*

**Library and Archives Canada Cataloguing in Publication**

Easson, Susan, 1963–
   The wise renovator : a homeowner's guide to managing contractors and home renovations : save time, money and, possibly, your marriage... / Susan Easson.

"Renovation Management Company".
ISBN 0-9737343-0-2

   1. Dwellings—Remodeling.   2. Dwellings—Maintenance and repair.
3. Contractors.   4. Consumer education.   I. Title.

TH4816.E38 2005          643'.7          C2005-903299-5

**Disclaimer:**
Renovation Management Company, CreativeWorks and the author assume no responsibility for any damages, injuries suffered or losses as a result of the information published in this book. Readers should be competent in evaluating the contents of this book and its application to their own situation and in accepting responsibility for any and all losses. Although Renovation Management Company has undergone exhaustive research, if any doubts or questions remain, readers should use their own judgment and/or consult local experts or authorities. Because local codes and regulations vary greatly, always check with local authorities to ensure that your project complies with all applicable local codes and regulations. Renovation Management, CreativeWorks and the author disclaim any and all responsibility for the application of the information.

Author: Renovation Management Company, Susan Easson
Publisher: CreativeWorks Publishing
Editors: Katherine and Bill Coy, Andrea Lemieux
Design, layout and print production: Heidy Lawrance Associates  **www.hlacreative.com**
Creative Illustrations: James Cooper
Technical Illustrations: Steve Corrigan, Crowle Art
Printed and bound in Canada

This book is owned by Renovation Management Company, a consultant in residential construction and contractor management.
Website: **www.renomanagement.com**

# Contents

Preface ...................................................................................................... 1

one    The Importance of Contractor Management .......................... 3

two    Defining Your Management Style .......................................... 9

three    Homework before Your First Contractor Meeting .............. 13

four    Understanding Your Contractor's Labor Costs .................... 23

five    Identifying Hidden Materials Markups ................................ 45

six    Building Basics: Know Your Project before You Delegate .......... 57

seven    Calculating Your Own Cost Estimate .................................. 93

eight    Deciphering Your Contractor's Estimate ............................ 125

nine    Negotiating, Signing and Maintaining the Contract:
The Essentials in the Game of Survivor .............................. 131

ten    Only the Honest Will Survive .............................................. 145

Appendix 1: R-Value Insulation and Square-Foot Coverage .......... 147

Appendix 2: Formulas for Remaining Structural Materials .......... 148

Appendix 3: Sample Finishing Materials Worksheet .................... 165

Resources and Recommended Reading .................................... 167

Index ........................................................................................ 169

# Preface

The inspiration for this book and the founding of Renovation Management Company was the result of personal renovation experiences, frustrations with abuses from contracting professionals and encouragement from many homeowners to share a method of managing a contractor and a home renovation project.

After having experienced both successful and challenging renovations and undertaken exhaustive research, I recognized that I was in an advantageous position of understanding the ins and outs of the construction industry. I realized that busy homeowners and first-time renovators are at their contractor's mercy when negotiating estimates, timelines and construction details. Many of us are not familiar with average contractor profit margins, honest and dishonest labor and materials markups and if the quantities of very expensive structural materials are accurate. We forget that contractors are our employees, entrusted with possibly thousands of renovation dollars, and that they need to be managed to ensure renovation success.

I founded Renovation Management Company to offer homeowners a consultancy service on residential construction and contractor management. I wanted to provide clients with insight and foreknowledge prior to their first contractor meeting and the start of their renovation project.

Thanks to the encouragement from many, I wrote *The Wise Renovator* to provide a consultancy service not only for clients, but also for readers across North America. It is my hope that this book helps you to recognize the importance of contractor management to avoid personal and financial disaster and paves the way for a successful home renovation experience.

*Susan Easson*

# 1 The Importance of Contractor Management

Are you planning a renovation project? Are you worried about escalating costs, incurring long delays and the quality of work? Your worries are justified, particularly in the chaotic world of construction.

During the past five years, home construction has soared to record levels. With demand exceeding supply, prices have skyrocketed, transactions have been made quickly—and mistakes have been made. The boom in construction can be attributed to baby boomers, who are settled into their long-term home and are looking to renovate rather than relocate. In 1996, David Foot, author of *Boom, Bust and Echo*, predicted a renovation boom stating, "Boomers will stay put and renovate...the result will be boom times for the renovation business." Later, Foot remarked that "boomers are a demanding lot and they won't tolerate shoddy workmanship." When I first started to write this book, however, I was amazed by how many people had experienced construction difficulties. Many had incredible stories and long lists of complaints about their contractor.

Unfortunately, with the current demand for construction services, contractors may be tempted to take on too many projects or cherry-pick the larger ones. No longer are contractors available to work on what are considered small projects. Homeowners experience struggles in simply getting a contractor to come out to the house for a project estimate. Further, once the contractor finally arrives, many homeowners are short on time, place trust in the contractor and give away the keys to the house. If contractors so choose, they are in a position to take full advantage of a trusting homeowner who is eager to have a project completed on time.

As witnessed during any stock market surge and plunge, frenzied demand can lead to substantial and, possibly, unethical profits. Today, the construction world is caught up in a surge and profits are running high. Patience in such a whirlwind is difficult. Many homeowners are kept waiting for months for a tradesperson to show up. Rather than enduring further delays, homeowners may feel pressured to move ahead and to take a risk with their money just to get the project done.

Once a contractor finally arrives at the door, distinguishing between the honest and the dishonest can be tricky. Even professionals in the business have trouble differentiating. A contractor friend told me that looks and personality are definitely deceiving since, in his experience, some of the most honest, professional-looking project managers turn out to be the most dishonest with clients. Because of the perceived complexity of construction, homeowners may turn a blind eye to a construction project only to discover quality and pricing issues after completion.

As an example, a neighbor of mine constructed a million-dollar home. After installation, a supplier accidentally forwarded an $11,000 bill for granite to the homeowner instead of to the contractor. Unaware that the homeowner had received the supplier's invoice, the contractor billed the homeowner $27,000 for the same granite. The question remains whether the homeowner would have paid the $27,000 if the supplier had not mistakenly sent the bill. Sadly, some homeowners don't have the time to check the accuracy of the estimate and the final invoices.

At first glance, understanding the world of construction may seem too time consuming and detailed to be worthy of study—an endeavor equated to reading a VCR instruction manual. Just paying somebody to do it would seem to be the preferred approach rather than delving into the business. Contractors can complicate matters further by talking about projects in "contractor speak." Many terms and descriptions contractors use can be confusing. With glassy eyes, we find ourselves nodding in agreement. Sometimes, we just don't understand what on earth is being said; yet, heaven forbid if we were to stop the conversation and proclaim it! With cash in hand, limited time and our pride to keep intact, we often prefer to pass the project to the first contractor to finally knock on the door.

*The old saying goes that we sometimes spend more time driving to Costco to pick up a cheaper $5.49 jumbo pack of cereal than focusing our energies on driving down the price of a project by thousands.*

Many people have luck with a hands-off approach. However, the old saying goes that we sometimes spend more time driving to Costco to pick up a cheaper $5.49 jumbo pack of cereal than focusing our energies on driving down the price of a project by thousands. For first-time renovators or home builders, up-front time spent on research will pay off in the long run. Speak to those who have gone through a major construction project and many would say they learned from their mistakes and would manage it very differently next time. However, most of us don't have the luxury of having a next time.

Unfortunately, during my first renovation experience, I found myself overcharged and nine months behind schedule. I was too late in the game to exercise anything but damage control. I realized that what I *could* do was help others avoid this situation by writing a book about how to put clients back in the driver's seat. Maintaining project control during boom times can be difficult. However, knowing how to work the system, understanding your project and turning on your negotiating charm can save you thousands of dollars and many frustrations.

The objective of this book is to allow you to benefit from the experience of others and to apply those lessons learned to your project. *The Wise Renovator* is based on the reality of the construction industry and is designed to help you foresee and avoid project pitfalls. You will gain insight as to why construction projects seem to sit idle for long periods of time and why homeowners roll their eyes during a construction conversation. Knowing what you are about to embark upon will enable you to more effectively manage your contractor. This book will help you to do the following:

- Define your managerial duties
- Recognize how to prepare for a construction project
- Discover how contractors can hide overcharges and excess profits in an estimate and in the final invoices
- Gain a general understanding of construction
- Learn how to complete your own cost estimate
- Discover how to negotiate with your contractor
- Save money, minimize frustrations and stress and gain peace of mind in knowing that you are in control

From a small renovation to the construction of a new home, you will be able to better manage project costs, quality and completion dates. Understanding the labor and materials required for your project is of utmost importance when negotiating an estimate. You will learn how to calculate a quick top 10 materials cost estimate or complete a full cost analysis. A top 10 estimate will provide you with the ability to quickly assess the accuracy of your contractor's quote and uncover any glaring errors.

Important in developing a contractor relationship is to "speak the speak" or "walk the talk." Becoming fluent (or appearing to be somewhat knowledgeable) in basic contractor language will help you to manage your project and drive down project costs. In negotiations, contractors can rely on your inexperience. You will have a definite advantage if you can challenge, for example, how much crushed stone is required prior to laying a foundation. Chapter 6 explains the construction of a house from the foundation to the roof without bogging down in do-it-yourself information. If you find that you have as much construction information as you require for your custom project, move ahead to chapter 7 and complete your cost estimate. Later, if you require more detail you can refer back to chapter 6 and dig deeper.

Having gained an understanding of the construction industry, you may discover that you have an interest in pursuing more information to even further improve upon your new-found skills. Further refining your own cost estimate would likely be the first place to start. The formulas provided in this book for generating a rough estimate are based on average retail pricing (USD) and labor rates. These formulas will allow you to challenge thousands of dollars in contractor variances. If you are interested in detailing costs to the final nail, you can easily continue your own research with the guide in appendix 2. Remember, however, researching your prices on your own will take you more time. Without question, the more detailed you are, the greater your savings.

In recent years, some contractors have taken advantage of homeowners and are making money hand over fist. Contractor's salaries have swelled and, since their services are in such high demand, even the most honest contractors can be tempted to take a few extra profits here and there. Whatever your project—big or small—you will find relevant information in this book to help you with your renovation.

Good luck!

# 2 Defining Your Management Style

*"We'll do the job for $10,000.....*
*$15,000 if your husband tries to help."*

- - - - - - - - - - - - -

So you have decided to renovate, build a new home or create a larger kitchen. The first step is to identify how you will manage your contractor. There are four possible approaches to contractor management:

1. The absent CEO: remain hands-off and let the contractor run the show.
2. General Manager: become actively involved with the contractor.
3. Ownership: operate as the general contractor hiring your own tradespeople.
4. Solo: work as the tradesperson and do it yourself.

## THE ABSENT CEO

The only advantage of this approach is that you save time. A hands-off approach works best with those who have limited time to get involved in decision making and project execution. As an absent CEO, a homeowner doesn't want to hear about delays or construction difficulties and rarely participates in problem solving. The contractor takes on full responsibility to get the project done. The major disadvantage, however, is the surprise bill at the end of the project. Costs have the ability to skyrocket all by themselves, and clients are left to foot the bill. In many cases, the homeowner may have difficulty enjoying the renovation because frustrations with the end result are not easily forgotten—they're hard to forget when one has to live with them every day.

## THE GENERAL MANAGER

Staying actively involved can help the project run in a more cost-effective manner. Usually, homeowners plan to actively participate in the project. For someone who has had construction experience or knows how to work the industry to their advantage, they may look forward to a personal project and perhaps to even working alongside the tradespeople. Forearmed with knowledge of factors such as materials costs, suppliers and tradespeople's hourly rates, the experienced homeowner can quickly calculate a rough project estimate.

However, most homeowners are new to construction and are about to embark on their first renovation project. These homeowners may plan to stay on top of the project, but encounter obstacles. With little construction experience, they may feel uncomfortable on site, become lost in materials and terminology details and have difficulty finding the time necessary to devote to the project. Frustrations are further exacerbated when costs go up, materials are not properly installed and the project lags behind schedule. Conflicts between the homeowner and the contractor may escalate to a point at which construction comes to a halt.

In an attempt to learn about a project, the homeowner may look to the contractor to provide insight. However, while I was researching this book, I frequently came across contractors who seemed to employ a strategy of confusion to win business. Project information and the to-do list are presented as rocket science until the homeowner, intimidated and overwhelmed, willingly hands over the project to the contractor.

But it doesn't have to be this way. Preparing for construction discussions by learning about what labor and materials are required will help you to more effectively participate in the discussions and better assess contractors.

Important in contractor evaluations is to have the ability to distinguish between those contractors who spend the time explaining the project in an understandable language and those who speak above the client's level of understanding. At your first contractor meeting, try to demonstrate that you have some familiarity with construction. For example, a down-to-earth discussion about different ways of moisture-proofing the basement will go a long way in developing a relationship. Those who already work in the industry or those who have a major renovation under their belt will have an advantage over those who do not. Fellow tradespeople and experienced renovators know how the system works, and frequently, services can be bartered. Demonstrating a level of understanding will help to even out the playing field and pave the way to honest discussions.

## OWNERSHIP

Employing yourself as the contractor and hiring your own tradespeople will save you a significant amount of money. To be successful, however, solid trade connections are essential. A booming construction industry means that access to specialized trades may be difficult. Unfortunately, when trade labor is in high demand, tradespeople prioritize work, remaining loyal to contractors with whom they have previously worked and who offer steady, repeat work (for example, a 200-home development project). Generally, tradespeople will work on the most profitable and convenient project. You may find that the wait times for trades are so long that the project comes to a complete standstill. Utilizing connections and creative incentives to attract tradespeople to your project may be necessary during the busy season.

Further, you will require a strong understanding of your project, including building order of operation and building codes—and a little engineering knowledge or experience wouldn't hurt. Depending on the project, you may be taking on a full-time job. I recommend that those who have little construction experience not hire their own tradespeople on a first big project—save that for your second. In this way, you can gain a tremendous amount of experience on your first project—you can develop trade connections and feel more confident in your abilities.

## SOLO

Finally, doing it yourself will bring the ultimate control and cost savings. However, finding the time is difficult, and many of us are not so skilled. Depending on the size of the renovation project, doing a project yourself requires an in-depth understanding of all fields of construction including electrical, plumbing, masonry and carpentry. A thorough study of building codes and the ability to read the schematics of architectural plans is required. For those who have a general interest and the time, doing a project yourself will save you a significant amount of money.

Bottom line, the success of any project is always affected by the effectiveness of its manager. Whatever management approach you plan on maintaining with your contractor, always bear in mind that your style can affect the success of your construction project.

The next chapter reviews essential steps to complete prior to your first contractor meeting and provides insight into the possible consequences of jumping into the unknown without being prepared.

*It was at that moment that Phil,*
*the contractor, felt he really hadn't*
*thought the project through.*

# 3 Homework before Your First Contractor Meeting

Congratulations, your first long-anticipated meeting with a contractor has arrived. For months—in many cases, years—you have lain awake at night dreaming of the wonderful possibilities of construction. Dreams of knocking out a wall here, installing a window there, building an extension or, perhaps, a new home. Whatever your preference, take a long, hard look at what is currently around you and decide whether you truly believe you have the stamina for a large project. Just ask any of your friends or family who have renovated—the dream of household changes can quickly become the reality of dust, mess and inconvenience for what can feel like a very, very long time. The end result can either leave you well pleased with your efforts or, due to lack of preparation and planning, leave you so disappointed with your project that you can no longer enjoy it.

One of the keys to success of any project is planning and preparation. Although the preparation required may sound like common sense, homeowners may rush through or skip the process altogether, feeling the pain later on. Consequently, prior to your initial meeting with the contractor, the following three steps should be completed:

1. Decide if you need your plans drawn by a professional.
2. Decide on the maximum amount of money you're willing to spend.
3. Plan on getting at least two other estimates.

## PREPARING THE DESIGN

Depending on the size of your project, you may want to consider hiring a professional architect or draftsperson to draw up plans. If you require a building permit, you must submit a professionally completed design for the city. (Guidelines differ in states and provinces.) Note that if your project is not large enough to require a building permit, a sketch drawing from either an interior designer or bathroom/kitchen retail store is helpful. Interior design software is also available in retail stores to assist you in creating a plan.

Having the design completed earlier rather than later has significant advantages, including:

- Identifies unforeseen complications
- Provides a basis for the contractor to work with and to quote on
- Helps avoid misunderstandings by providing you and your contractor with an exact picture of what is to be built
- Eliminates surprises and expensive creative endeavors that may not work
- Provides backup to legal contractual disputes and helps to settle disagreements, either prior to or during court

Find a professional who is recommended by friends or neighbors. Or, if they can't help, you could consider approaching an impressive looking worksite, knocking on the door and asking the contractor the name of the professional who completed the plans. Having the right architect, who will complete much of the upfront work, will save you time and confusion down the road. For major construction projects, good architects are worth their weight in gold. You will be forced to think through details that you may not have considered, saving you delays and rework on site. Meetings between the architect and contractor can be incredibly beneficial in determining the most creative yet cost-effective approach to solving construction problems. Architects can present unique, exciting designs; good contractors should be able to quickly assess the cost effectiveness and participate in problem-solving alternatives. One of a homeowner's jobs is to make trade-offs—weighing design alternatives against construction costs and priorities. Having a good architect in a meeting alongside a competent contractor will save you money in the long run.

Architect's fees vary according to the reputation of the architect, the size of your project and the level of involvement. The ideal situation is to find a young architect who has had experience on your type of project and has strong references. If you are lucky, the architect's fees may not be as high as one who has a solid reputation and has been in the business for many years. Ideally, you are receiving the same level of service at a lower price. Instead of a lump sum, many architects apply a cost per square foot. The better the reputation, the higher the price per square foot. Within these fees, map out all the services that are included and comparison shop.

To save money, a draftsperson can also complete the necessary drawings for building permits at a fraction of the price. A draftsperson will provide the required engineering drawings for you and your contractor. You may find, however, that the drawings may look flat—missing some of the creative architectural details. Thumbing through magazines and pulling out some of your favorite pictures can help fill in where the draftsperson has left off.

The disadvantage of employing draftspeople for a major renovation is that you may be required to make more on-site decisions. Large on-site decisions may increase the probability of costly errors and time-consuming rework. For those of you new to construction, having a draftsperson complete a major renovation is very risky. Second-time renovators, who know exactly what they want and feel comfortable working their way around a job site, would be in a better position to take advantage of a draftsperson's services.

If you prefer hiring an architect but your funds are tight, consider employing an architect for only the initial creative drawings and then using a draftsperson to complete the interior blueprints and the remainder of the project. One of the main reasons to hire a good architect is for the outstanding creativity applied to the initial drawings. Once the initial drawings are completed and agreed on, the architect will proceed to draw numerous blueprints for areas such as electrical, structural framing and plumbing. Since less creativity is needed for blueprints, it is a common practice for on-staff draftspeople to finish the work for the architect. Fees are generally higher for the architectural firm to finish the blueprints than if you were to find your own draftsperson.

Another route to consider is ordering plans from a house magazine. If you can overcome the feeling that this is an impersonal way to build a home, the advantages can be significant. The cost savings can be tremendous. For example, I interviewed a homeowner who was planning on building a 4,000-square-foot home and preparing to spend approximately $40,000 in architect fees for a top quality architect. For a comparable-sized home, plans and blueprints from a house magazine were approximately $1,000.

You may worry that the end result may have a cookie-cutter, mass-manufactured appearance. But, putting your concerns aside, look through a few of the magazines—if not just for design ideas. Ensure you purchase the correct magazine applicable for the country you are planning to build in. Any well-stocked magazine rack carries a variety of home plan magazines for both United States and Canada. When ordering your plans, ensure that they are complete and can be used to obtain city building permits, and check the fees for customizing the plans.

One of the greatest benefits of utilizing a magazine plan is the bill of materials that can be supplied for an additional fee. The remainder of this book reviews the importance of producing your own cost estimate to use in comparison with a contractor's quote. Having the bill of materials already prepared for you will save you a great deal of time and effort.

## YOUR BUDGET

The second item to prepare is your budget. Additions and subtractions during construction are almost unavoidable, but the amount of preplanning will help to reduce last minute decisions. Frequently, experienced renovators state that costs can run 30% over the initial quote, while some insist you should just double the amount. The amount over budget can be financially crippling. However, the more preparation you do, the smaller the chance of costly surprises and the "might as wells." The "might as wells" are common during renovations. You may have heard some already, for example, "Since we're putting up halogen lights we might as well put five lights up in the hall too." Or, "Since we're here tearing down that wall we might as well keep right on going and tear down this wall too." Unfortunately, such spur-of-the-moment decisions add up very quickly. In many cases, they are neither properly quoted upon nor written into the contract. Secondly, frequent unplanned changes can cause long delays. Of course, everybody adds a few items here and there, but it is important to be aware of how disruptive project changes can be.

*Relying on others, such as your contractor's competition, to come forth and identify lowball estimates is unproductive.*

All of us have heard about contractors lowballing an estimate to win the business, only to state later that the quote didn't include what was expected. All of a sudden, costs have doubled to get the project done. One of your contractor management responsibilities is to evaluate the accuracy of your contractor's estimate. Relying on others, such as your contractor's competition, to come forth and identify lowball estimates is unproductive. In order to effectively negotiate an estimate you must go through the exercise of understanding the labor and materials costs for your project. Only then will you be able to identify realistic, honest quotes and lowball quotes. Without this understanding, you will have difficulty comparing one quote against another and you will only be able to negotiate the total.

Negotiating the total is a mistake. You may end up awarding the business to the contractor who submits the lowest number. A quick and easy solution—but nothing is said about the quality and quantity of construction materials and labor. Once you are completing a contract, you will be at a loss about what details to include. The contractor knows where the fat is within the estimate and what he or she plans on including in the contract—you have no idea. As long as the contract reflects the total agreed upon, not too much is left to negotiate.

The industry has come up with rough per-square-foot averages to build a new home. A figure of $120 per square foot is often used to provide homeowners with a rough estimate. Unfortunately, this estimate can be misapplied. As contractors frequently quote a total per-square-foot cost, homeowners have come to accept the average without questioning what was originally included.

For example, does the $120 cover only structural materials or are finishing materials such as flooring, bathroom fixtures, kitchen cupboards and appliances included? What does $120 per square foot mean? Different opinions about what the amount covers will be offered to you not only by the contractor, but also by another homeowner who has completed a major construction project. A first-time renovator's job is to evaluate differences between estimates with the objective of maximizing returns on the $120. Details of materials and labor included within the $120 should be clearly spelled out within the contract. If not, once construction commences, the homeowner may discover possible items that should have been included. Without a doubt, the more knowledgeable you are, the more control you gain, and the better the chance of staying within budget.

# THREE RECOMMENDED CONTRACTORS

The third preparation item is to interview three recommended contractors. Even a contractor who comes with recommendations needs to be carefully evaluated. The misdirected granite invoice discussed in chapter 1 involved a well-established, high-profile executive home builder who had worked on numerous renovations in the area. An innocent handover of an itemized invoice can be filled with such hidden markups. Contractor relationships need to be professionally maintained even if you are employing a relative or have had previous positive experiences. The following illustrates this scenario.

Right from the start, a contractor saved his client thousands of dollars on a retaining wall project. The contractor had friends at a nearby hotel who were blasting rock and could ship the boulder rock at no charge. Trust in the contractor's prudence and financial management was immediately established; however, as a result, the trusting client took his eye off the bottom line and was later taken to the cleaners in hidden charges.

The moral of the story is that one should spend the time researching contractors since first impressions can be misleading. You can contact the Better Business Bureau to determine if any complaints have ever been lodged against a particular construction company. You can find your local Better Business Bureau in either United States or Canada at www.bbb.com. Another informative website is The National Association of Home Builders at www.nahb.org.

Also, be wary of the references you receive from a prospective contractor. If possible, try to find three or four independent references within your neighborhood—or from someone you know. I have interviewed people who have told me that some references turned out to be friends, relatives or even employees working for the prospective contractor. As a starting point, below is a list of questions to ask of references:

- How did you locate your contractor?
- Why did you select the contractor and did the contractor meet your expectations?

- Are you related to, employed by or a long-time friend of the contractor?
- What were some of the frustrations you experienced? How were they solved?
- How did your contractor solve on-site problems? Were you satisfied?
- Was the contractor on schedule and on budget?
- How did the contractor budget for contract changes and did you feel the amount was clearly explained and realistic?
- Have you had any structural problems and did the contractor respond in a timely manner to fix the problem?
- Would you hire this contractor again?

Finding three recommended contractors to come out to your house will be time consuming, but very worthwhile.

Having done your preparation, the doorbell rings and your first prospective contractor arrives at the door. Review the plans, judge the contractor's experience and accept any creative input offered. Negotiating with your contractor is reviewed in chapter 9, but remember, the more time the contractor spends now, the greater the commitment to the project. Time invested benefits all involved.

On the other hand, don't feel pressured to choose one particular contractor because you have already invested a significant amount of your personal time. Be aware that you will probably spend more time with the first contractor because you are excited to get the project moving and you are enthusiastic about receiving as much input as possible. Chances are you will not spend as long with the second contractor, and by number three, you may find that you are bored and ready to move on. Impatient, you may end up choosing the first contractor since the whole process has become too time consuming.

For the sake of your project, tenacity helps. Try your best to evaluate each contractor equally. Keep a list of questions by your side. Pertinent questions that will be discussed in more detail throughout the remainder of this book include:

- How long have you been in business?
- What, if any, tradespeople do you have working for you who are available at an hourly rate? If none, is all project work subcontracted out?
- How long have you been working with your subcontractors? (A long-standing relationship may indicate that the subcontractors may prioritize your contractor's jobs.)
- Have you ever worked on a similar project?
- Do you see any construction challenges right at the outset? (The answer will provide you with an indication of willingness to explain construction questions in plain language.)
- How many jobs will you be working on when mine is underway? Do you predict business to slow at certain times over the next year? (You will need to judge the priority of your job versus the others in relation to the size of the contractor's company.)
- What format do you use in laying out a quote? (Assess how comfortable the contractor is with detail. As a homeowner, you are striving for as much detail as possible.)
- Are you tax exempt? (Check your local state and provincial tax regulations. In some areas, as long as the contractor is purchasing and installing materials, local tax rates are not applied on materials.)
- Do you have construction insurance? (Ensure the contractor has both on-site theft and fire insurance and workers' accident compensation insurance.)

Answers to the above questions, particularly regarding the tradespeople/subcontractors employed and the format of the quote will help pave the way to understanding your contractor and the components that will be used to complete an estimate. Chapter 4 defines tradespeople and subcontractors and provides an in-depth explanation of the trades.

Lastly, before you close the door on your initial contractor meeting, discuss how long the quote will take and schedule a follow-up meeting. Follow-up meetings help to anchor a timeline and gain a commitment to return. Since contractors are in high demand they may have difficulty finding the time to return phone calls. Ensure that you secure a follow-up meeting before the contractor leaves.

The next three chapters will address the importance of understanding how a quote is calculated and how markups are applied. After you complete these chapters, you will have a good idea of how much contractors make on a project. In fairness, contractors are in business to make a living. The question becomes how much is too little, reasonable or unethically excessive? The rest of the book will help to provide you with answers to these questions.

# 4 Understanding Your Contractor's Labor Costs

*"His estimate was the lowest, but he has to be home by six to finish his homework."*

The presentation of the quote initiates one of the most interesting discussions that you will have with your contractor. Many homeowners believe that the quote is a tangible document that finally gets the project moving. In anticipation, we look forward to the meeting and to discussing the finer details of the project. Unfortunately, without an understanding of how contractors calculate an estimate, negotiations may come to a standstill.

Contractors are very knowledgeable in their field, and inexperienced homeowners frequently and blindly trust what is presented. Many times the details of a construction project can be confusing, and we rely on the contractor's expertise. For example, how many of us know the number of cubic yards of cement needed for a project's foundation—80 or 300? From a negotiation standpoint, the contractor holds all the cards and the client is at a disadvantage. We ask a few questions, nod our heads and think, "Wow, I can't believe how expensive this is." Having already spent a great deal of time with the contractor, we continue on rather than start all over again with another contractor.

The benefit of reviewing the information in this book is that you will be able to manage and control costs by completing your homework prior to receiving the quote. You will be able to hold your own and effectively negotiate a contract that benefits both parties. Done properly, you should be able to identify disreputable contractors. You will have the choice of whether you want to continue with a dishonest contractor or hold out and wait for one who will treat you fairly.

Contractors can use a variety of methods to produce a cost estimate. Some estimates are well prepared and detailed while others are not. In many cases, the creation of the quote requires a combination of calculations that can be confusing when presented. Try to be flexible yet completely thorough in reviewing every line item. A successful contractor requires not only trade skills, but also strong business acumen. The smart contractor will know exactly where money is made within the estimate.

*Whatever the contractor's method, you need to prepare your own rough estimate in order to challenge what the contractor presents. Your own estimate should reflect costs that are as close to the actual project invoices as possible.*

Accordingly, contractors may hesitate to provide full estimate disclosure. Answers to pointed questions may be vague, or with dishonest contractors, the answers may be misleading. Try your best to treat the quote as a science rather than a general guesstimate. As mentioned earlier, the more detailed the quote, the easier it is for you to evaluate. Whatever the contractor's method, you need to prepare your own rough estimate in order to challenge what the contractor presents. Your own estimate should reflect costs that are as close to the actual project invoices as possible.

At the end of day, your estimate is composed of only two *major* components: labor and materials (sometimes referred to as "T and M"—time and materials). Understanding how labor and materials have been calculated and how honest and dishonest markups can be applied is critical in maintaining cost control.

Awareness that your estimate totals have been calculated from costs within only two areas—labor and materials—brings clarity and organization when evaluating a quote.

Whether the contractor provides a breakdown of labor and materials or whether you calculate the numbers independently, in order to evaluate the competitiveness of a quote, you need to analyze all the components that created the totals. We will review the labor side of the equation first and cover materials in chapter 5 as it is a large topic and can definitely be an area of excess.

A contractor's labor estimate is composed of three major categories:

1. Contractor's management fees
2. Hourly tradespeople
3. Subcontractors

The amount estimated for each of the above varies according to the size of your contractor's company and the size of your renovation project.

## CONTRACTOR'S MANAGEMENT FEE

When evaluating an estimate, your contractor should explain his or her operations and review the categories that were included within the labor calculations. Smaller projects require fewer tradespeople and less of the contractor's management time. Smaller companies should have fewer cost components and should be easier to assess. Mid- to large-sized companies are frequently employed on larger renovation projects that involve complicated project schedules, labor and materials management and higher administrative fees. In general, the larger the contractor, the higher the management fees and markups. Below are costs included in project estimates for small, mid-sized and large companies. Notice the additional management fees and markups included in project estimates generated from larger contractors.

### SMALL CONTRACTORS

➢ The smaller contractors are usually the on-site tradespeople. The contractor who produces the quote is the primary tradesperson who completes the job. The estimate does not usually include a project management fee. The smaller contractor charges an hourly fee, and the labor estimate is a projection of how many hours the project will take multiplied by the hourly rate. Materials are frequently estimated at cost. If the small contractor is not certified for specialist work (for example, electrician or plumber), the contractor will find the required tradesperson. The certified tradesperson usually charges by the hour, and the homeowner pays the tradesperson separately. The contractor's estimate includes the following:

---

**SMALL-SIZED CONTRACTOR ESTIMATE**

    Contractor's fee ($ hourly rate × # of projected hours)

    Certified tradespeople ($ hourly rate × # of projected hours)

    Materials cost

+   <u>Tax</u> (rates on materials and labor vary by state and province)

=   $ Total project estimate

---

## MID–SIZED CONTRACTORS

➤ Mid-sized contractors should be employed on larger projects and are in high demand among baby boomers and first-time renovators. While the material presented in this book applies across all sizes of contractors, we predominately focus on relationships with this group.

Mid-sized contractors are more involved in project management and may or may not work on site alongside tradespeople, as smaller contractors do. A project management fee is paid for the management of all labor and materials with the objective of maintaining the estimates and timelines as outlined in the contract. Contractors can employ a variety of methods to calculate project management fees. A common practice, referred to as the cost-plus method, applies a percentage to total project costs. For example, 10% may be applied against the total estimated project cost ($300,000) to determine the project management fee ($30,000). The problem with this approach is that, in order to make money, the contractor expects to purchase all the finishing materials for the homeowner, including such items as flooring, countertops and perhaps, even appliances. If the homeowner purchases these items, the contractor expects to receive the invoices for them and bills the homeowner 10% of the cost of these purchases. In theory, this cost-plus approach appears simple, but in practice, many homeowners resent paying the contractor a percentage on materials they have researched, purchased and delivered. To correct this problem, most reputable, mid-sized contractors charge a higher percentage—for example, 25% to 30%—on specific costs (labor cost plus structural or contractor-purchased materials cost before tax). In other words, a contractor adds all estimated labor and structural materials, multiplies the total by 25% to 30% and adds this amount to the project estimate. The project management fee covers the contractor's overhead expenses (such as wear and tear of bulldozers, and equipment, tires and administration) and profit from the job. Usually, 15% of the 25% to 30% management fee covers overhead, leaving the contractor with a 10% to 15% profit. Once the dollar amount for project management fees has been determined, the homeowner could consider negotiating a lower fixed-rate dollar amount. To increase negotiation success, the homeowner needs to ensure the contractor understands that if any changes were made during the construction stage, a defined adjustment, as outlined in the contract, would be applied to the contractor's fixed-rate fee. The advantage of charging a higher percentage on labor and structural materials versus a lower percentage on all costs is that homeowners are not committed to purchasing all materials through the contractor and have the freedom to buy their own finishing materials without the contractor pestering them for the amount they spent.

To determine estimated labor rates and costs, depending on the size of a renovation project, the mid-sized contractor can either employ hourly tradespeople, hire subcontractors or a combination of both. Employed hourly tradespeople work for the contractor's company and usually receive employee benefits, including insurance and workers' compensation. A contractor would need to be large enough and provide steady employment to be able to afford an employee payroll. If a contractor were to take on employees, the majority of contractors would start by employing general tradespeople or carpenters. Carpenters work on the general wood frame of your house, including floors, ceilings and roof, and are frequently the largest percentage of your total labor cost for large renovations. Other general tradesperson responsibilities may include daily site cleanup or assistance to other trades. If a contractor is large enough, he or she may employ other specialized trades including drywallers and painters.

Subcontractors are those trades that the contractor doesn't have under his or her employment. Examples of subcontracted tradespeople are masons, plumbers, electricians, brick layers and stucco applicators. When contractors prepare project estimates, they would contact the required subcontractors, explain the subcontractor's job and request an estimate. A subcontractor may work alone on site and bill an hourly rate or, if large enough, hire hourly employees to complete the job and add a subcontractor management fee to the estimate. Larger subcontractors usually submit estimates to contractors as a fixed price or on a per-square-foot rate.

The more subcontracting, the more layers between the contractor and the tradespeople and the more expensive the labor. A mid-sized contractor's project estimate may include the following:

**MID–SIZED CONTRACTOR ESTIMATE**

  Cost of tradespeople ($ hourly rate × # of projected hours)

  Cost of subcontractors

+ Cost of structural or contractor-purchased materials (see chapter 5)

= Total contractor project cost before tax

  Contractor's project management fee (25% to 30% × project cost)

  Contractor's markup on structural materials (see chapter 5)

+ Tax (rates on materials and labor vary by state and province)

| | |
|---|---|
| = | Total contractor estimate |
| + | <u>Cost of finishing or homeowner-purchased materials</u> (see chapter 5) |
| = | Total project cost |

## LARGE CONTRACTORS

➤ Large-sized contractors/developers are set up for new multi-home construction. They are involved in purchasing and developing large tracts of land. The quantity savings in materials are more than offset by labor markups on the layers of management between the contractor/developer and the tradespeople. Remember, on-site tradespeople are usually paid by the hour. However, with developers, project managers are employed to manage tradespeople and subcontracting managers. Subcontracting managers are employed to manage the subcontracted tradespeople. The total project estimate may include the following:

**LARGE-SIZED CONTRACTOR ESTIMATE**

| | |
|---|---|
| | Developer's fee |
| | Project manager's fee |
| | Cost of tradespeople ($ hourly rate × # of projected hours) |
| | Subcontractor's management fee |
| | Cost of subcontractors |
| | Cost of materials and developer's materials markup (see chapter 5) |
| + | <u>Tax</u> (rates on materials and labor vary by state and province) |
| = | Total project estimate |

Having divided contractors into three defined categories does not mean that variations of the above do not exist. Depending on the economic situation, contractors are flexible in adapting their business from project to project. The possible layers of management that can be included in your project estimate can vary from one contractor to the next.

How a contractor chooses to structure his or her organization is up to the contractor. However, the onus is on you to understand the structure and to evaluate the estimate to determine if the quote is accurate or if there are hidden markups. In order to effectively evaluate the labor estimate, you need to understand not only a contractor's organizational structure, but also the industry profit averages and labor rates. If you employ a mid-sized contractor, a breakdown of the labor estimate by project management/contractor fee, hourly tradespeople and subcontractors is required in order to effectively negotiate the estimate.

*How a contractor chooses to structure his or her organization is up to the contractor. However, the onus is on you to understand the structure and to evaluate the estimate to determine if the quote is accurate or if there are hidden markups.*

For example, two estimates may be equal in total cost, but the labor components that were used to calculate the total may be very different. One contractor's quote may budget for subcontracting your entire project, whereas another's may reflect the same total labor cost, yet that contractor will employ only his hourly tradespeople. The latter quote appears to have a larger hidden contractor profit than the first. Directly employed tradespeople usually provide more of a profit to the contractor, hence, more room for negotiation. Identification of the areas to negotiate is the first step in reducing project costs.

Further, ensure that you hire a contractor who is appropriate for the size of your project. For a small renovation, try to avoid hiring mid- or large-sized contractors. For kitchen and bathroom renovations, employing large contractors who typically build 3,000-square-foot homes could result in paying hefty markups. At a minimum, you will incur a 25% to 30% project management fee. In addition, your project may be given a lower priority than the larger, more profitable jobs, and you may experience long wait times for tradespeople.

The best scenario for smaller projects is to find a small contractor or general tradesperson who is known to be reputable by your friends or neighbors. A retired tradesperson who is looking to keep busy and make extra money on the side can be the perfect candidate. If you are lucky, the small contractor will charge just for daily time and materials at cost.

Another benefit to working with small, reputable contractors is that they have contacts with other trades. Only the reputable contractors seem to have a wide network of connections. A contractor without contacts may be a telling sign about the quality of work you will receive. Once you have found a small, reputable contractor, don't let this person go since such contractors are few and far between.

Project management fees for mid- to large-sized contractors should be discussed first and written into the contract, otherwise, you may end up hiring a contractor who charges higher than average markups and you may be shocked by the final invoices. One homeowner showed me an estimate and only after I encouraged her to ask about markups did she learn that the contractor had applied a 50% project management fee. Without asking the question and establishing a percentage, you may not even be aware that a large markup was quoted and paid.

When negotiating the percentage, remember that contractors may add profits in other areas of the quote to further improve their bottom line. Ideally, if you are employing a mid-sized contractor, try to hire contractors who contractually agree to a 25% to 30% project management fee and don't try to profit from your project in other ways. One way to make some extra cash is within the other labor components. Adding markups within the hourly tradespeople's and subcontractors' rates is done either as per contractually agreed upon or added into the base rate without the homeowner's knowledge. Therefore, the next step is to explore how mid-sized contractors budget for hourly tradespeople.

## HOURLY TRADESPEOPLE—PROJECTED COSTS

When a contractor presents a project estimate, in order to assess the accuracy of the calculations, you will need to separate, and to understand, the quoted amount for hourly tradespeople and subcontracting. The amount for hourly tradespeople has been calculated with an average hourly rate multiplied by the number of projected hours. Knowing how the number was calculated, you can ask the contractor two specific questions:

- What trades do you have under your employment?
- How many work days have been budgeted for each trade?

Answers to the above questions will allow you to gauge whether the labor estimate for hourly tradespeople is reasonable. Reasonable is important since accuracy in calculating an estimate is difficult due to the variability of labor. For example, general tradespeople/carpenters are paid an average *daily* rate of $300. Table 4.1 lists hourly rates for other tradespeople based on national U.S. average *contractor-employed* labor rates. Hourly rates are usually slightly higher than negotiated daily rates. Rates can vary by state or province and according to the economy. Although these rates can be used for your rough estimates, research into current rates within your area will increase your cost accuracy. You can search on the internet and download regional rates at sites such as www.craftsman-book.com. For further confirmation, competitive hourly rates may be printed in your local newspaper's classified section under headers such as "General Help Available." Developing a relationship with several tradespeople who work in the aisles of your local building supply store may also be worthwhile. Ensure during your conversations that you are receiving contractor-employed hourly trade rates as opposed to homeowner house-call rates. Since contractors can offer steady and more secure employment, the hourly rates a contractor pays for tradespeople are much lower than the house-call rates paid by homeowners.

**Table 4.1    Average Trade Labor Rates**

| TRADE | HOURLY RATE (USD) |
| --- | --- |
| ▮ General tradespeople (framers, carpenters or millwrights) | $21–$32 |
| ▮ Electricians | $31–$35 |
| ▮ Plumbers | $32–$35 |
| ▮ Masons | $27–$31 |

| | |
|---|---|
| ▮ Drywall installer (Sheetrocker) and taper | $27–$31 |
| ▮ Painters | $29–$33 |
| ▮ Bricklayers and bricklayer helpers | $21–$33 |
| ▮ Excavators (operating engineers) | $34–$38 |
| ▮ Roofers | $30–$34 |
| ▮ Plasterer and plasterer helpers | $22–$32 |
| ▮ Tile or floor layer | $28–$30 |
| ▮ Truck driver | $24–$28 |

If your contractor states that your project will require three to four carpenters per work day, then your average daily carpenter labor cost will be about $1,000 per day ($300 × 3 to 4 carpenters). If your contractor states your project requires 60 work days, the amount budgeted for carpenters should be approximately $60,000. Remember, your estimate is an approximation to identify major variances.

Small (10%) variances may be a result of an honest overestimation to cover potential disruptions. Also, the contractor may have accidentally included other labor (for example, an electrician) with higher labor rates, within the carpenter's estimate. However, larger variances may be a result of a questionable contractor looking for profits over and above the 25% to 30% project management fee.

## SUBCONTRACTORS

The third category in a contractor's labor estimate is subcontractors. As mentioned earlier, your contractor may hire only subcontractors for your project. A subcontractor's estimate is usually presented as a per-square-foot or flat rate. Occasionally, with smaller subcontractors, an hourly rate is quoted. A per-square-foot rate or flat fixed price includes materials, hourly tradespeople and a subcontractor's fee. For example, your subcontractor may estimate $7 per square foot to stucco a 2,000-square-foot area. The subcontractor will have calculated the total cost of materials to cover 2,000 square feet, the total labor cost (the hourly rate multiplied by the number of hours) and the subcontractor management profit or fee. All these costs added together provide the flat rate or, by dividing by 2,000 square feet, produces the $7 per-square-foot rate (see table 4.2).

**Table 4.2   Subcontractor Estimate** • (Stucco application for 2,000 square feet)

| | |
|---|---|
| Materials cost | $4,000 |
| Labor ($30/hr. × 2 tradespeople × 80 hrs.) | 4,800 |
| Subcontractor management fee | 5,200 |
| Total flat/fixed rate | $14,000 |
| Per sq. ft. ($14,000 ÷ 2,000 sq. ft.) | $7 |

Understanding how a per-square-foot rate is calculated opens up questions about the accuracy of your contractor's subcontracting estimate and discussions about how to reduce the rate. Chapter 7 provides formulas for calculating your project's labor and materials costs. For those trades that your contractor plans to subcontract, you will be able to evaluate the competitiveness of the per-square-foot rate by dividing your applicable labor and materials costs total by the applicable number of square feet.

A subcontractor's management fee is usually an opportunity for negotiation. The fee can be a result of honest charges for management and work/materials warranties. However, this fee can also be inflated to pay contractor kickbacks that a homeowner has not contractually agreed to. Kickbacks are usually paid by the subcontractor as a reward for the business. Your subcontractor may forward an estimate to your contractor that includes a hidden contractor markup. You would pay the final invoice to the contractor who then deducts the kickback and forwards payment to the subcontractor. As long as you have completed an estimate analysis, kickbacks and markups can be identified within a subcontractor estimate. However, to the unsuspecting homeowner, kickbacks may go unnoticed, and to further compound the problem, a contractor may apply a 25% to 30% contractor management fee markup.

The contractor's markup to subcontractor fees is negotiable in the same way that the 25% to 30% project management fee is. In your negotiations, remember that you can always find your own painter or plumber if the fee is unreasonable.

The ideal situation is to reduce or eliminate subcontractor management fees. As mentioned, most of the larger subcontractors manage on-site tradespeople and charge management fees on top of the project cost. To lower the subcontractor's labor charge, you should encourage your contractor to employ small subcontractors who work on site as tradespeople. Every layer between the on-site tradespeople and the contractor applies a markup. The fewer layers between the tradespeople and your contractor, the lower the final labor charge.

A solution to reduce large subcontractor management fees is to employ your own tradespeople. As mentioned earlier, having a retiree or family tradesperson can work to your advantage. However, consideration must be given to work/materials warranties. One of the reasons subcontractors' fees are high is the inclusion of after-job warranties. A problem may be encountered when the contractor resents homeowners' hiring their own tradespeople. Blame for inferior quality work may be directed toward tradespeople the homeowner has hired. For example, a homeowner may hire window installers and later discover one of the windows is cracked. The question becomes, who fixes the window? Is the crack a result of how it was installed or a mistake by the contractor's tradespeople? I had a situation where my own tradesman installed some plumbing, but the contractor's tradesmen took some of it apart to install insulation. Hiring your own subcontractors requires strong communication between the contractor, his or her tradespeople and those

*Hiring your own sub-contractors requires strong communication between the contractor, his or her tradespeople and those you have hired to prevent order-of-operation errors.*

you have hired to prevent order-of-operation errors. Although this is a definite solution to reduce submanagement fees, you need to be aware of the possible conflicts that may arise.

Having evaluated and agreed to the project management fee, general tradespeople and subcontractor estimates, the next contractual topic to consider is whether the total amount estimated for these three labor categories should be fixed at a flat rate or left open as a variable cost. Another option is combining fixed pricing for subcontracted work and variable pricing for hourly general tradespeople.

## FIXED RATE LABOR

With fixed labor estimates, a total labor charge will be agreed upon and not exceeded unless authorized in writing. Your initial discussions about the details of what is included within the flat rate are critical and must be documented in the quote. However, there are both advantages and disadvantages of fixed rate pricing.

### ADVANTAGES

One advantage of a fixed rate labor charge is that you know exactly how much the project will cost. Further, you save on time and aggravation since you do not have to keep track of hours spent or debate the point with your contractor. If you have a rental property, cottage property or you are working full time, you may not have the time to closely supervise the project.

### DISADVANTAGES

The disadvantage is that you may start to wonder where the workers are and whether the labor estimate was inflated. The contractor may have honestly padded the labor numbers to protect his or her profit against unforeseen complications. For example, when excavating, an existing basement wall may collapse. The contractor who signed a fixed rate contract would have to repair the damage out of pocket. For protection, the contractor may increase the fixed labor estimate to cover such risk.

On the other hand, the numbers may have been inflated in attempts to improve the bottom line. The contractor may dishonestly present a fixed labor contract knowing that the projected labor cost is higher than the actual number of hours required to finish the project. For first-time renovators, determining the accuracy of a fixed labor contract can be difficult without having an understanding of the number of hours required to complete a job. Receiving competitive quotes, asking questions and clarifying variances to your own estimates will help in the evaluation. Whether or not the actual numbers were calculated honestly, to cover risk, or dishonestly, the contractor will rarely refund the excess if the project was completed on time or ahead of schedule and under budget.

Another disadvantage of fixed pricing is that a disreputable contractor might scrimp on labor and materials in order to further improve the bottom line (for example, applying one coat of asphalt sealer instead of two). The information presented in this book should help you to keep on top of the job quality.

With fixed pricing, you may also find that you are constantly debating what was included and what was not included in the price. At the outset, all details to include in the contract are difficult to foresee, but with a fixed price you will be required to lay out all agreements. You may have forgotten to mention that the corners need to be rounded, or maybe you did mention it, but it was overlooked in the contract. Now you find yourself in the dilemma of either paying extra for the work that was somehow missed or continuing on and settling for less. Fixed pricing requires a tremendous amount of detailed forethought and imagination. A solid drawing or an existing model home found in a new development will help to ensure that items are not overlooked.

If you use an existing model home as your prototype, your contractor's estimate would be based on the exact reproduction of the model home's interior and exterior. If any issues crop up during the building stage, you can revisit the model home and point out what your contractor missed. This would eliminate haggling and frustrations about what was included in the estimate since you have a model as an example.

*Fixed pricing requires a tremendous amount of detailed fore-thought and imagination. A solid drawing or an existing model home found in a new development will help to ensure that items are not overlooked.*

Further, attention should be given to the estimate accuracy of the project additions in a fixed contract. Your contractor and his or her tradespeople may have already agreed to a fixed rate payment for your project. If you want changes made to the original plans during construction, your contractor may charge a premium to the homeowner, but the tradespeople end up doing the work for free. Your contractor may tell the tradesperson just to work on the addition and that the payments will be evened out on the next job. Very little can be done about correcting this, but this inside information can be helpful when assessing a potential expensive adjustment to a fixed contract. Unfortunately, if you are set on making a change to the project during construction, you may have little choice but to accept the premium. With a fixed contract, the importance of a complete and detailed plan to minimize on-the-spot additions can't be overstated.

## HOURLY OR VARIABLE LABOR

A more cost-flexible project is an hourly based contract. In some cases, the entire labor quote is hourly. In other cases, you may agree to a combination of hourly, flat or per square foot. Most often, the hourly component of the contract is for the general tradespeople/carpenters—the largest percentage of total labor costs for major renovations.

An hourly contract means that the contractor will still be required to calculate out the total labor cost with a labor breakdown; however, the contract becomes an estimate rather than a fixed, contractual amount. The clock starts ticking as soon as the project commences, and labor charges are paid out based on the hours put in.

## ADVANTAGES

The advantage of the hourly based contract is that you still require a labor estimate, but the labor charge for the project *may* be lower in the long run, as long as you keep on top of the project. In theory, you should be paying for actual hours spent on the project.

When the project commences, the hourly numbers start to accumulate. Critical to your hourly contract is to keep a daily log of the number of workers and the hours put in. Further, you should compare your totals with the contractor's on a weekly basis. If you forget for a month or two, you will find it hard to remember what was done and you will be at a disadvantage when the contractor's numbers are different from yours.

Within the contract, outline dates to meet and review the hourly totals. It is important to communicate that you plan to monitor the work.

You may prefer an hourly rate for the peace of mind that the quality of the job may be superior to that of fixed pricing. You may believe that the contractor, knowing his or her labor is paid hourly, will avoid cutting as many corners. The point is debatable, but I do believe that with an hourly contract the contractor is not as pressured to scrimp and save.

A remaining advantage to an hourly contract is that the "might as wells" discussed in chapter 2 are somewhat easier to work into the project. Whether big or small, all projects have changes. In a fixed contract, an amendment to the contract needs to be signed. With an hourly contract, you should definitely receive a written estimate, yet the work can commence immediately and be added to the hourly charge. However, remember to constantly revisit your totals to ensure you're not getting carried away with too many additions.

## DISADVANTAGES

You may be concerned that, with an hourly contract, the employees will take their time completing the job. This may be true, and you need to ensure they are logging actual time spent and work completed. Remember that the contractor's job is to project manage. In order to get paid, the contractor is usually motivated to finish the project as quickly as possible. An important element to add to an hourly contract is a financial incentive to complete the project on schedule. Of course, disruptions can happen that cause setbacks (for example, bad weather, strikes, additions made to your projects and accidents) and delays will occur. Chapter 9 reviews methods to keep the contractor motivated to stay on the job.

Further, you can run into trouble if you are unable to track the hours worked. If you have hired a dishonest contractor, you are at his or her mercy when the labor hours are billed. You have no way of knowing how many workers and how many hours were put in. If you can't keep track of hours spent, then you will need to work out a solution to keep your contractor honest.

Having reviewed the three major labor components—project management fees, hourly tradespeople, subcontractors in a fixed versus variable contract—let's examine some more questionable methods contractors may employ to improve their bottom line.

## SUSPICIOUS LABOR PRACTICES

### HIRING UNQUALIFIED TRADESPEOPLE

Contractors may make more money if they hire cheaper, unqualified labor at a lower hourly labor rate but charge you a higher rate for certified tradespeople. For example, a tradesperson who completes electrical work may be electrically handy but not a certified electrician. The contractor may charge you a certified electrician rate, pay the tradesperson a lower rate and pocket the difference. To avoid this, you should include in the contract that all tradespeople must be certified in the work they perform.

## CHARGING FOR WORK NOT PERFORMED

In a variable contract, a disreputable contractor can make money by charging for excess hours and work not performed. Keeping track of your project should be the responsibility of your contractor; however, when also responsible for his or her own income on the project, the contractor may be tempted to charge for more hours than actually occurred. Further, contractors charge project management fees to labor costs. Homeowners end up paying not only for the work not performed, but also for the project management fees attached to the inaccurate labor costs.

## SUBCONTRACTOR KICKBACKS

A contractor may add a percentage markup or a couple of dollars per square foot to the subcontractor's estimate without having the client's agreement. Another trick is that the subcontractor may have a built-in kickback to the contractor hidden within the estimate. You should be able to identify excesses if time is spent analyzing the subcontractor's estimate. However, to the unsuspecting homeowner, kickbacks may go unnoticed within the subcontractor's estimate. When contractors apply the 25% to 30% contractor management fee to the subcontractor's estimate, the homeowner ends up paying a management fee on top of the kickback.

## FAILURE TO PAY EMPLOYEES FOR CHARGED TRAVEL TIME

A contractor may charge you for employee travel time to and from the worksite, but not pass the fee on to the employees. Determining this unethical charge is difficult unless you ask the employees. Despite the difficulties, an agreement on payments for travel time should be included in the contract. Some insist on a charge for travel time, particularly if the site is fairly remote (for example, a water-access cottage). Another often overlooked point of negotiation:

the contractor will charge the same hourly rate for travel time as for the skill itself. In other words, the cost of sitting in a car becomes equivalent to building a stud frame wall. To illustrate the cost benefit of reducing travel time—if you apply an hour's drive to and an hour's drive from (per employee) in the $60,000 labor scenario, the homeowner would pay an additional $14,000 in travel time. Reducing the travel time labor rate by half would save you $7,000. The frustrating part is that you can't be sure if the contractor is pocketing travel time or is actually paying out to the employees.

## PROFITING FROM THE HOURLY LABOR RATE

In a variable contract, as long as contractually agreed upon, the contractor can make extra money from the hourly labor. In negotiations, the contractor may prefer to lower the project management fee percentage in favor of increasing the hourly labor rates.

For example, the contractor may agree to lower the management fee by 5% in return for adding $5 per hour per tradesperson. Applying this to the $60,000 labor scenario, if the contractor makes $5 per hour on the tradespeople, based on an 8-hour day, the contractor can make about $10,000. On the flip side, the contractor has given away 5% in project management fees. If the total projected labor and materials costs were $120,000, the contractor would lose $6,000 on project management, but gain $10,000 on labor.

Profiting from hourly labor rates is a frequent occurrence. However, difficulties arise when you are not aware that inflated rates have been paid. Hard to assess is whether the contractor is making extra money on the hourly labor rates despite having a contractual agreement against the practice. Determining how much has been added is difficult, since asking a tradesperson employed by your general contractor how much he or she is being paid by the hour is just not done. The contractor's employees will hesitate and may refuse to respond to avoid getting caught between agreements you have made with their employer. Opinions vary about whether the practice of paying inflated rates despite contractual agreements is acceptable. The industry seems to indicate that the contractor is almost always making a few extra dollars on the labor rate, whether the homeowner is aware of it or not. Awareness of the process and familiarizing yourself with local trade labor rates will help when you are assessing the accuracy of the contractor's labor estimate.

*Avoid getting the contractor disgruntled, otherwise, he or she may not be motivated to work on your project or the quality of work may slide.*

It is important to remember that if the contractor is happy (and you are happy) with all contractor fees, every other item should fall into place. Your objective is not to catch your contractor in the act of dishonesty; rather, the objective is to negotiate a fair contractual agreement. Avoid getting the contractor disgruntled, otherwise, he or she may not be motivated to work on your project or the quality of work may slide.

Having covered how to interpret and demystify the labor side of the balance sheet, the next chapter reviews the second component of your contractor's estimate—materials costs. Without a doubt, contractors can hide excessive markups within this area. The next chapter will take a closer look at how contractors calculate materials costs and give some hints on how to differentiate between practices that are fair and those that are questionable.

# 5 Identifying Hidden Materials Markups

*"What's the difference between the $10 tile and the $15 tile?"*
*"Five dollars."*

- - - - - - - - - - - - -

So where can contractors really make the dough?—In the materials. An estimate is a projection of total labor costs and total structural materials costs and a budget for finishing materials. One of your top priorities for effective cost and contractor management is to become familiar with the structural materials required for your project, your materials costs and where hidden markups can be found within the estimate. Without an understanding of what goes where, the materials estimate cannot be effectively discussed or negotiated. Problems frequently arise because finding the time to understand the quote process and to prepare a detailed contract that will minimize opportunities for dishonesty may be difficult.

Materials can be divided into two categories: finishing and structural. Finishing materials are those items that you are generally required to purchase or select (for example, windows, kitchen cupboards, countertops, flooring, tubs, faucets, lighting and fireplace inserts). Usually the contractor has provided a budget for these items within the quote. The purpose of providing a budget is to illustrate how much has been allocated for finishing materials and to enable the contractor to produce a total project cost. Remember that you are the one who makes the purchasing decisions on finishing materials. Negotiating a finishing materials budget amount that the contractor has supplied within the estimate is like negotiating with yourself. For example, *you* will ultimately make the final decision about whether to install the $7- or $4-per-square-foot maple hardwood.

All other materials that the contractor purchases, such as concrete, insulation, drywall and lumber, are referred to as structural materials. The importance of understanding the structural materials required for your project can't be overstated. The primary purpose of hiring a contractor is for the installation of these materials. What and how structural materials are to be installed is the essence of a contractor's estimate.

Structural materials can be very costly, particularly lumber and concrete. For example, if you use concrete for foundation on a 3,500-square-foot home, the concrete can cost close to the same amount as your kitchen cupboards. Usually the contractor has purchase control over structural materials. Negotiating these materials, particularly if you are a first-time renovator, can be difficult unless you have a basic knowledge of construction. Many larger contractors will produce a computer-generated estimate. This adds to the authenticity of the quote, but now both the computer and the contractor's expertise must be challenged. This can be somewhat intimidating, and with little construction expertise, most of the negotiations then tend to revolve around finishing materials—not a completely productive exercise.

Unfortunately, homeowners are less interested in the structural parts of the house, preferring to concentrate on items such as windows and flooring—which tend to be much more interesting than discussing the thickness of concrete. In defense of those who avoid learning about structural materials, the books and courses on the topic can be overwhelming in do-it-yourself detail. Building basics presented in chapter 6 provides an illustrated summary of only the necessary construction information required to produce your own quick cost estimate.

The reality of the situation is that managing your contractor requires not only knowledge of basic construction, but also an understanding of the estimate for structural materials and a detailed review of every invoice against the estimate during the construction stage. Inexperienced homeowners may experience difficulties not only in determining the accuracy of the quote for structural materials, but also in comparing the actual partial payment invoices against the estimate total.

For example, a total amount for lumber will be provided in the estimate, yet you may be required to make an interim payment upon completion of the foundation and first floor. In amongst many other structural materials, the partial payment will include a bill for the lumber purchased. However, since more lumber will be required for the second floor, determining how the partial payment compares against the total lumber quoted can be time consuming and difficult. Upon completion of the project, a few suspicious homeowners may attempt to add and compare the total actuals against the estimate, but adding potentially hundreds of structural materials across a variety of invoices from different time periods is unappealing. Instead, inexperienced homeowners may accept the rationale that the changes made during construction affected the quote or that wastage was higher than anticipated.

Many opportunities exist for a contractor to dishonestly pad the structural or finishing materials that may be purchased, either during the estimate or when the actual invoices are forwarded to you. On the other hand, many contractors are honest and put in a hard day's work. A contractor can honestly increase a project's profitability from materials as agreed to in the homeowner's contract or through the contractor's suppliers or manufacturers. Unfortunately, the dishonest contractors are downright sneaky and give the industry a bad reputation. The honest contractors suffer from the clients who have been taken advantage of in the past. These clients give future contractors a harder time, and hence, the client becomes "difficult" in the contractor's eyes—a Catch-22. Dishonest contractors are bad news for the industry as a whole.

The advantage you have is the understanding that preparing your own estimate and completing a detailed and accurate contract is all within the responsibilities of effective contractor management and successful project management.

This chapter provides insight into both the legitimate and suspicious markups that can be included within the materials estimate or during the construction invoice stage. First, let's review the standard, legitimate methods that contractors may employ to improve the profitability of a project.

# STANDARD METHODS

## MATERIALS MARKUPS

A percentage markup can be applied to the structural materials costs (before tax) for purchasing and delivering. Since you spend the time researching and purchasing finishing materials, a contractor markup should not be applied to these materials unless your contractor is purchasing and delivering the products from preferred suppliers.

In many situations, even an honest contractor may fail to mention that a percentage markup to pick up and deliver materials has been added. A markup of 10% is very reasonable, 30% is average and 50%+ is exorbitant. The markup is negotiable based on the difficulty of the project, having to pick up from various suppliers, the location of your project relative to a major city centre and the difficulty of transporting the materials to the site (for example, to a water-access cottage). Also, the materials percentage is negotiable alongside the contractor's 25% to 30% project management fee (see chapter 4). The management fcc is on labor and structural materials *costs*. If you agree to a materials markup over and above a project management fee, ensure that the project management fee is applied before the materials markup and tax. Both the markup and tax amounts should be recorded as separate line items on your estimate and invoice. Further, the markups should be clearly detailed in your contract.

## SUPPLIER KICKBACKS

Most of the time, you are not the contractor's first client. A contractor's suppliers, such as the building supply stores, may offer financial incentives or kickbacks for purchases or store loyalty. Although debatable, kickbacks are a fair and honest way for a contractor to make extra profit. Some feel that the contractor should pass on kickbacks to the client. Yet supplier kickbacks are a result of store relationships that have been built up over many years, representing the hard work with previous clients, and have very little to do with your project. Determining the amount of kickback the contractor receives is difficult. Whether it is fair or not depends upon your viewpoint. As long as your materials costs remain competitive with other suppliers, kickbacks are considered fair. However, you may want to let the contractor know you are familiar with the process when negotiating the contract.

## MANUFACTURER KICKBACKS
Contractors can also make extra money by remaining loyal to certain manufacturers. Volume rebates and financial incentives are given to contractors who purchase and install the manufacturer's brands. From halogen lights to fireplaces, contractors may install the same brands from one project to the next. As long as the brand is right for the client, a manufacturer kickback is a win-win payment.

## VOLUME DISCOUNTS
Purchasing in bulk frequently saves money. Contractors usually work on several projects at one time and the materials required may be similar. Instead of buying just the small quantities required for your project, the contractor may combine your order with another and receive a volume discount. The discount may or may not be passed on to the client.

The following are some of the questionable methods and suspicious markups contractors may employ on materials. Remember that many contractors are honest and upfront, but arming yourself with as much information as possible makes good sense in this overheated market. Buyer beware.

## SUSPICIOUS METHODS AND MARKUPS

### EXCESSIVE MATERIALS MARKUPS

To the unsuspecting client, contractors can charge a higher than average materials markup. A materials estimate may include an unknown percentage markup applied to the cost of every line item. Failure to challenge the contractor's materials calculations leads clients to acceptance of a number that has been, in some cases, purely estimated and fabricated. Failure to understand structural materials hinders a homeowner's ability to negotiate a quote. To illustrate the point, I was presented with a bathroom renovation estimate to review; the quote was vague with totals of $8,000 for labor and $7,000 for materials. The materials sounded about right until she told me she was purchasing the tub, toilet and faucets. The materials quote from the contractor was for everything else including items such as piping for plumbing, drywall and tiles—untouchable structural materials that the average home-owner has trouble defining. Since drywall is $10 for 32 square feet and piping is $0.58 per foot, I had trouble bridging the gap to $7,000. Questioning her contractor, she learned that a 55% materials markup was applied. A higher number was probably used, but the message here is not to accept materials totals without having prepared your own estimate. Since bathroom materials are expensive, on the surface, a $7,000 estimate doesn't seem high; however, only upon questioning are we able to break down the quote and get a better deal.

As with labor, a materials estimate should be presented in detail and the amount of materials markup should be contractually agreed to. Also, ensure that the contractor's project management fee has been applied to materials costs before materials markups and tax have been applied.

### PROJECT MANAGEMENT FEES APPLIED TO ALL MATERIALS

When your contractor presents your initial estimate, a standard practice is to apply a project management fee to *all* structural and finishing materials. Problems arise when fees are applied to materials that you end up sourcing and paying for directly to the supplier. Most homeowners spend hours researching finishing materials such as hardwood floors, lighting, faucets and tubs. By funneling your supplier's bills through your contractor, although contractors receive supplier discounts, you end up paying a 25% to 30% project management fee even though you have done all the work. In a fixed or variable contract, ensure you indicate the finishing materials that you are responsible for purchasing and remove both the budgeted amount for these materials and any contractor management fees that may have been applied. Also, include that project management fees are to be charged only on contractor-purchased finishing and structural materials.

The project management fee is still applied to labor since your contractor is usually responsible for the coordination of the labor to install all structural and finishing materials unless you indicate otherwise. For example, if you decide to employ your window supplier's installers to guarantee the window installation warranty, ensure that you have detailed this decision within your contract and that project management fees on the labor to install the windows are not charged.

## DISHONEST SUPPLIER INVOICES

Once the project commences, the contractor is required to purchase materials for the job. Typically, materials are purchased from a few suppliers with whom the contractor has developed a strong business relationship. The suppliers are paid from the contractor's own pocket, but the amounts paid are recorded on a separate invoice that is sent to the client for payment. In other words, the contractor pays the supplier and then the contractor bills you.

The problem arises when contractors are working on multiple job sites at one time. Usually, the contractor will order materials in bulk and then divide and deliver the materials to the various job sites. The supplier's invoice reflects the bulk merchandise purchased; however, the contractor requires a separate invoice for each homeowner. Upon the contractor's instructions, the supplier, as a favor, may choose to complete separate invoices that reflect pricing and quantities delivered to the contractor's individual clients. Over time, as a faster process, the supplier may give the contractor blank invoices to be completed. The contractor is now required to divide up the supplier's bulk invoice, filling in blank ones for the clients. The contractor may fill in the invoice correctly—or not, since the probability of clients uncovering an error is very slim.

You may overlook asking for backup to the contractor's numbers. Although you may think this is common sense, you may not have the time to invest in cross-referencing many different materials against a variety of supplier invoices. Further, the contractor may recognize that his or her own suppliers won't be able to provide you with pricing and quantity information. Having found myself questioning invoices that appeared inaccurate, I phoned suppliers to verify the information. I quickly realized that suppliers hesitate or refuse to get involved in a contractor's invoicing. Even if the supplier was aware of what materials were delivered to whom, details about such things as pricing and markups are unknown to a supplier. The prospect of losing a contractor's loyal business by getting involved in client–contractor relationships is too risky. The question becomes how to determine if the invoice is accurate. The only method is to have produced your own estimate using competitive retail pricing and to calculate materials quantities to use as a guide to compare against the final invoices.

## CHARGING FOR EXCESS MATERIALS

You may recognize a materials pricing error more readily than a materials quantity mistake. The contractor may choose to fill in the supplier pricing accurately, but the quantities may be overstated. For example, a shipment of 50 boxes of shingles may have been delivered to the worksite, but only 35 were used and the rest went home with the contractor. The homeowner may receive the invoice for the 50 boxes.

I have heard stories of contractors building themselves a new home with the amount of excess materials left over from previous jobs. Or, excess materials have been ordered and paid for by one client, with the leftover sent and billed to the next client; the contractor ends up being paid twice for the same materials. This is a common occurrence. It could be anything from a few hardwood boards left over and used to build a new entrance somewhere else to a larger quantity of materials. Many people are unaware of how the system can go wrong. Uncovering the overcharge is difficult if the materials have already been installed. In many cases, the contractor's bills are received after installation and clients generally overlook the idea of counting quantities used.

As an example, I learned about an overcharge for roof shingles only after calculating the area of our roof and by calling the supplier to determine how many square feet a $25 bundle of shingles covered. I discovered that I was charged for an extra 20 bundles of shingles, or 600 square feet. This wouldn't sound like much for an unsuspecting, first-time renovator, but on a 1,500-square-foot roof, an extra 600 square feet is excessive. Once I added on materials markups, project management fees and tax to the materials cost of the extra 600 square feet, I was looking at about a $1,000 overcharge on just the shingles alone.

Structural materials, particularly lumber, require an understanding of construction. Homeowners usually don't crawl up into the attic to verify the number of 2 × 12s installed. Even if the 2 × 12s were counted, the contractor orders lumber as needed over time, and the homeowner would have to cross-check every invoice to calculate the total quantity ordered.

Armed with the understanding of how possible overcharges can creep into your bill, you will be better prepared when reviewing the estimate and keeping a watchful eye on invoices as the project commences.

## CHARGING TAX TWICE

When materials are sent to the contractor, the supplier forwards the invoice (or the contractor completes the invoice) and the total amount is transferred to your bill. Watch out for a simple, yet sometimes overlooked miscalculation. Standard state, provincial and federal taxes (unless the contractor is tax exempt) have already been applied on the cost of materials from the supplier invoice, so ensure that the contractor does not lump the total labor and materials costs together and apply tax to the grand total. Ask for all the supplier invoices to back up the bill the contractor forwards to you. Ensure that the appropriate tax is applied to either the supplier's or contractor's invoice and is not charged twice.

## CHARGING FOR TAX DESPITE CONTRACTOR EXEMPTIONS

In some states and provinces the government will not apply state or provincial taxes to materials bought and installed by the contractor. The contractor must qualify and receive a purchase redemption certificate that exempts the contractor from tax at point-of-sale. In some cases, the contractor may turn around and show retail sales tax on the materials purchased even though the contractor was not required to pay it. You will need to ask your contractor if he or she is tax exempt. The answer can be verified with your local city revenue and taxation department. You should also become familiar with construction taxes and ensure that the correct percentage is applied to the applicable category.

## CHARGING FOR MATERIALS WITHOUT SUPPORTING SUPPLIER INVOICES

Your contractor needs to supply all backup supplier invoices to support charges that have been recorded on your contractor's invoice. For example, one homeowner told me that several times he found amounts on his bill that didn't have supplier invoices attached. Realizing the error, the contractor reduced the bill by $3,000. His contractor informed him that since the invoice was lost, the cost would be absorbed. Feel sort of sorry for the contractor? It is very possible the invoice never existed, because a quick phone call to the supplier for a duplicate invoice could have solved the problem. Check for any addition mistakes—simple, but effective in reducing costs. Make sure to get out your calculator and add the totals to ensure your contractor has added correctly.

Many of the questionable methods contractors may employ may sound far-fetched to the average homeowner. However, after exhaustive interviews with frustrated homeowners, I found these were the most frequently heard situations. Unavoidably, construction projects seem to almost always commence during a homeowner's busiest period, when work schedules or personal lives seem particularly hectic. Dishonest contractors may attempt to slip through unethical charges as we rush through invoices and construction discussions.

Awareness of contractors' most popular tactics, and understanding that you are entrusting a contractor with tens and possibly hundreds of thousands of renovation dollars, should launch your home construction project to the top of your priority list.

The most important element to a successful renovation is to stay on top of all aspects of your project. None of the above questionable practices may surface, but being aware of the possibilities of what *can* happen, can be your best defense. Now, time to put the hard hat on.

# 6 Building Basics: Know Your Project before You Delegate

In order to participate in construction discussions and negotiate an estimate with your contractor, a simplified understanding of home construction is essential. Understanding basic construction provides you with the ability to identify the necessary structural materials and labor required for an elementary project and for a more complex, customized venture. From a small renovation to a new home, the construction fundamentals are similar and consistent.

This chapter explains materials required for a construction project. Like making a layer cake, building a home is the assembly of materials in a predetermined order of operations— one material laid on top of the other until completion. Just as one layer of the cake is the same as the other, the frame construction of the floor, walls and ceiling of one storey is the same as the next.

A contractor is hired to install these materials and to alleviate worry about accuracy in aligning and leveling. Although it may be helpful to have a construction degree or experience in construction, an effective estimate evaluation doesn't necessarily require a comprehensive knowledge of angles, spacing and building codes. Let the contractor worry about construction details while you concentrate on the materials and getting a feel for the approximate number of labor hours required to complete your project. If you find you have a keen interest in pursuing more detailed information beyond what is presented in this book and what your contractor has explained, complete do-it-yourself books are available that provide extensive installation specifics. Employees at retail and building supply stores can also provide you with assistance.

*Although it may be helpful to have a construction degree or experience in construction, an effective estimate evaluation doesn't necessarily require a comprehensive knowledge of angles, spacing and building codes.*

Having spent a tremendous amount of time and money in retail chain stores, I would recommend selecting a store that educates and trains employees to work in specific aisles or construction trades. Well-trained employees, who are responsible for customers within one aisle, seem to be more willing to spend the time to answer customers' questions. I recall an employee actually sitting me down in a back room for an hour explaining the details of roof construction. In retail chains that fail to adequately train employees, I would frequently be faced with empty aisles or find only unqualified employees or students working part time available to answer questions. The building supply stores listed in your local telephone directory will also supply you with information. Patience is required at building supply stores since the employees are accustomed to servicing local tradespeople.

This chapter has been divided into three major sections including the basement, the floors/storeys and the roof. Within each section, the construction of the floor, walls and ceilings are explained with consideration to electrical and plumbing requirements. The order of explanation does not necessarily equate to the order of operations on the job site. All contractors have their own order of operation dictated by the architect's plans, building codes, labor availability and the contractor's completion schedule. Upon signing a contract, the contractor will include a project schedule. Contractor incentives to complete a project on schedule are discussed in more detail in chapter 9.

# FOUNDATION

A foundation is the substructure of a house that minimizes the impact of ground shifting and prevents the walls from collapsing. In the past, foundations have created dusty basements that stored grandma's old furniture, never-to-read-again books and old golf clubs. Today, basements have been transformed into functional living spaces with an office, play area and dust-free laundry rooms. You look upon a basement as a living-space opportunity; however, your contractor's priority is to build a solid, moisture-proof foundation.

The design of a foundation can accommodate for a full basement, crawl space or above-ground support posts. Full basements are the most popular—many prefer having the full headroom, the extra storage space and the option of finishing the basement. Crawl spaces don't sound too bad—until after about five years, when shuffling into a dusty 2-foot-high space to retrieve a box in the back seems unappealing.

Both a full basement and a crawl space require a backhoe to dig a hole; whether the hole is 2, 4 or 10 feet deep, the equipment cost is the same. Labor, however, will be slightly higher for a full basement since more hours are required to dig a deeper hole and to build a higher block wall. The materials cost differential of a block wall, in absolute dollars, between a crawl space and a full basement is not significant in the grand scheme of things. However, the cost differential of a full concrete wall versus a block crawl space is significant since labor and materials for concrete and the installation are expensive. You can assess the differences and decide what best suits your needs.

## FULL BASEMENT: FLOOR

- Excavate/dig the hole.
- Build the footings: A footing is required to contain the basement floor and to support the walls of the house. A footing resembles a train track outlining the perimeter of the house. The basement walls rest on top of the track and the basement floor is poured

in the center area. The track, or footing, is constructed from wood and is frequently 2 ft. wide and 1 ft. deep, but depends on the size of the basement walls. Rebar (long, 1/8 in. to 5/8 in. thick steel bars) is required to reinforce the concrete. The rebar is positioned in the hollow wooden footing frame with attention to ensure that the rebar will be covered with at least 3 in. of concrete, but doesn't sit on the bottom. Cement is poured into the wooden frame.

○ Pour gravel: The first layer to the basement floor is 1/2 in. or 3/4 in. gravel. The gravel is poured approximately 4 in. deep (varies by state and province—check local codes) within the inside area and along the outside perimeter of the footings. The gravel on the outside of the footings acts as a diffuser to help keep the inside basement dry.

○ Install jack posts: Jack posts are simply clay-colored steel posts that run from floor to ceiling to support the first floor. The architectural plans will indicate if and where jack posts are required. These posts can't stand alone in the center of a concrete floor; they require the construction of a separate wooden box made from 2 × 4s. The posts are set into the center of the box and cement is poured to fill the box area.

○ Lay down a vapor barrier: The purpose of a vapor barrier is to prevent moisture from entering unwanted areas. A vapor barrier is usually made from some sort of plastic, but can come in different shapes and sizes. For use under the concrete floor, the vapor barrier is generally clear sheets of plastic that can be purchased in 150 ft. rolls. This type of vapor barrier can also be referred to as plastic sheathing.

A tougher two-ply, high-density polyethylene can be installed to further improve moisture resistance.

○ Lay Insulation: Installation of 1/2 in. thick, rigid extruded polystyrene as a layer on top of the vapor barrier is optional. The insulation helps to keep the concrete floor somewhat warmer.

○ Moisture-proof the basement: The construction stage is the time to ensure that the proper materials have been installed to help keep moisture out of the basement. The inside water must be able to drain out of the house and the outside water must be directed away from the foundation walls. The inside drainage system should be installed prior to pouring concrete since cutting the concrete later on can be messy, time consuming and expensive.

**FOUNDATION: Typical Interior/Exterior Moisture-Proofing**

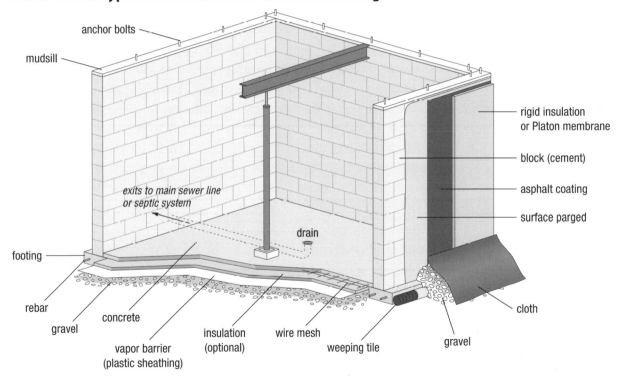

anchor bolts

mudsill

rigid insulation or Platon membrane

block (cement)

asphalt coating

surface parged

*exits to main sewer line or septic system*

drain

footing

rebar

gravel

concrete

vapor barrier (plastic sheathing)

insulation (optional)

wire mesh

weeping tile

gravel

cloth

## Inside: Moisture-Proofing

Water can enter the basement either from the outside or from an inside source such as a washing machine. A round, 4-inch floor drain should be installed at the lowest floor elevation (if the basement slopes) that connects to an ABS or PVC drain pipe. ABS or PVC is just a plastic material that has replaced traditional cast iron or copper. (In some states and provinces ABS is no longer installed.) Your ground elevation and local building codes will dictate the various acceptable methods to drain the water out, but commonly, your drain pipe runs under the concrete to either a sump pump or to the house sewer. Sump pumps push the water out of the house and end at an under- or above-ground location on the property. Or a basement drainage pipe may simply connect to the house sewer pipe and travel out to the main street sewer line.

A sump pump is a mechanical devise that sits in a sump pit (a metal or concrete-like bucket) that is sunk into the basement floor. The underground ABS/PVC pipe is connected to the sump pit. As water enters into the floor drain and travels along the pipe into the pit, the pump will automatically kick on when the water level fills up to a certain height. The pump pushes the water up through a sump pump hose that runs through the basement wall to the outside.

## Outside: Moisture-Proofing

To prevent water from entering the basement from the outside, weeping tile is laid on top of the gravel beside the footings around the entire outside perimeter of the house. Weeping tile is a fancy name for a 4-inch plastic pipe with holes punched out on the top. In some cases, the weeping tile is surrounded by cloth to prevent sand or dirt from entering, in other cases, weeping tile arrives as a standard perforated pipe and the cloth is laid down under and around all the gravel. The weeping tile ends at a predetermined distance away from the foundation walls. Any rainwater that may pool close to the house will seep underground, eventually reaching and traveling through the holes in the weeping tile. The water will follow along inside the weeping tile and will funnel out underground. Any excess water that may have missed entering the weeping tile is absorbed and diffused by the gravel underneath.

○ Pour the cement: To reinforce concrete, wire mesh (6 sq. in. steel mesh) or rebar may be set down on top of the vapor barrier or insulation and is supported to prevent the rebar from sinking when the concrete is poured. Typically, a concrete foundation is 4 in. thick (local codes vary). To note, cement is an ingredient that, when mixed with sand, gravel and water, hardens to concrete, yet contractors frequently refer to cement and concrete as one and the same. The concrete mixture may arrive premixed in a truck or the contractor may haul in the dry ingredients and mix on site.

○ Install floor finish: To finish a concrete basement floor, the contractor can either construct a subfloor or lay down a preassembled one. If constructing, sleeper studs

## FOUNDATION: Typical Floor Finish

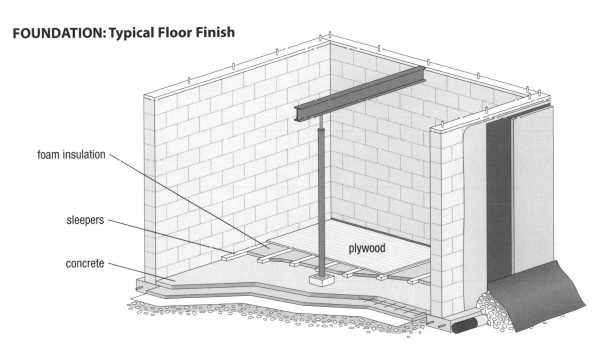

foam insulation

sleepers

concrete

plywood

(2 × 4s placed width side down, 12 in. apart) are placed on top of the concrete floor. Insulation is usually installed between the studs; however, if extruded polystyrene was installed underneath the concrete, this layer can be considered optional. A layer of plastic sheathing (vapor barrier) is laid down on top of the sleeper studs and insulation or can also be installed underneath the sleeper studs on top of the concrete floor. Plywood, usually 3/4 in. thick 4 × 8 sheets, is fastened on top of the vapor barrier.

○ As an alternative, Drycore, a preassembled subfloor, is available in 2 × 2 ft. square tongue-and-groove boards and has the vapor barrier (a black platon membrane) already glued to the plywood. Tongue-and-groove is a frequently used construction term defining the fit of one board to the other—a small concave groove (like a half pipe) is on one end and the other board end butts or fits into the groove. When laid on the floor, the boards fit together and masonry fasteners are used to secure the Drycore to the concrete floor.

○ The most popular basement floor finishes are carpet or vinyl. Due to moisture concerns, hardwood is not recommended for basements. Carpeting requires underpad on top of the subfloor and vinyl requires an adhesive (glue).

## BASEMENT WALLS

○ Build the walls: Basement walls are usually either block or solid concrete (local codes may limit your options).

### *Block Wall*

A block wall is made from 1 ft. long concrete cinder blocks or from a new product called ICFs (insulating concrete forms). Prior to laying cinder blocks, rebar is inserted vertically, every 24 in., into the concrete footing to help secure the blocks when laid. A 1/2 in. layer of mortar mix is spread on top of the footings and the ends of the cinder blocks are also "buttered" with mortar as the wall is constructed.

## *Insulating Concrete Forms*

ICFs have the same shape as cinder blocks except ICFs are made of a lightweight foam material. The material appears similar to the white Styrofoam used for coffee cups. The forms also sit directly on the footing and rebar is used for reinforcement. Cement is poured into the cavities of the ICFs. The benefit of using the forms is the high insulation value—R-value as high as 40. R-value is a measure of the insulating capacity of a building material; the greater the R-value, the better the resistance to heat loss. Some homeowners have installed ICFs up to the roof, replacing the typical wood frame exterior wall. ICFs are more costly in labor and concrete materials to install than cinder blocks. An argument can be made that installing cider blocks with polystyrene insulation on the outside of the basement wall and fiberglass baton insulation on the inside will achieve comparable R-value insulation to ICFs.

## *Concrete Wall*

Concrete foundation walls are generally installed in new home construction or larger renovations since the labor required to set up the forms and the materials cost of the concrete can be expensive. A concrete wall requires the assembly of a wall shell into which the cement can be poured. The shell is constructed from standard 2 ft. wide wooden forms (the height of one form is determined by the desired wall height) that rest on top of the footings. The forms are banded together and run along the entire footing. Once installed, the wooden forms look like the basement wall except the inside is hollow. Rebar is inserted into the forms for reinforcement.

An allowance for basement windows is required prior to pouring the cement, since cutting the concrete later on can be expensive. Wooden frames, built to the size required for the window openings, are inserted between the forms to block the poured cement from entering into the window space.

Oil spray is applied onto the forms to prevent the concrete from sticking. Once the cement has set, the forms are detached and hammered off.

○ Install window frames: Prior to installing the basement windows, wooden frames are secured to the concrete or block wall window openings. The 2 × 4 wooden frames support and protect the window.

○ Install window wells: Window wells are required to keep the soil and moisture away from the window. A well is either a standard metal liner attached to the outside foundation wall with masonry fasteners or a wood well that is constructed on site. A 1 in. drain pipe is installed vertically underground below the window and connects down to the weeping tile to prevent water from pooling at the bottom of the well. A 6 in. layer (local codes vary) of gravel is poured into the bottom of the well.

○ Finishing the basement walls on the outside:
  • Parge and apply an asphalt coating: Parging is a layer of cement applied on the entire block surface. Two coats of parging are trowelled or "combed" on. A solid concrete wall doesn't require parging. An asphalt coating, a black tar-like substance, is applied on top of the parged or solid concrete walls. Another product called "Blue Stuff" is more expensive, but tougher and more scratch resistant than asphalt.
  • Install drain screen (optional): As an extra layer, contractors may secure sheets of rigid fiberglass/polystyrene, or black plastic known as platon membrane on top of the asphalt coating or Blue Stuff. The screen helps the water run off the wall down to the weeping tile. The screen also helps to protect the asphalt coating from being scratched during backfilling and serves as an added insulator.

○ Finishing the basement walls on the inside:
  • Build a 2 × 4 stud wall (or 2 × 6 to improve thickness of insulation): The first layer on the inside of the block or concrete basement wall is the stud wall. The wall is made up of 2 × 4s, 16 in. apart. Of interest, the description is always larger than the

## FOUNDATION: Typical Interior Wall Finish and Ceiling/Floor Framing

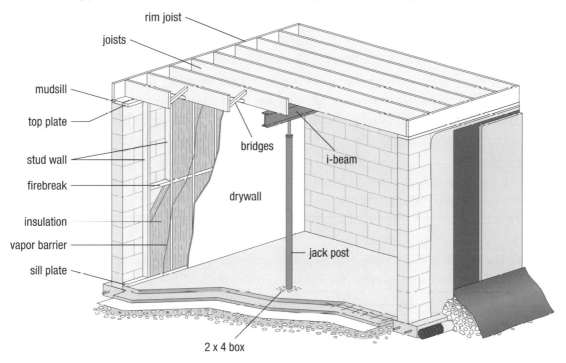

actual size of the board. For example, contractors refer to boards as 2 × 4s, yet the actual measurement is 1 3/4 × 3 1/2. Some contractors recommend pressure-treated wood to improve moisture resistance and 2 × 6s to improve the R-value of the insulation installed. The 2 × 6s are spaced 24 in. apart and provide extra depth to install a thicker, higher R-value insulation. With 2 × 4s, insulation with an R-value of R-13 or R-15 is installed. With 2 × 6s, the R-value can be increased to R-19 or R-21.

Agreement about the size of studs and type of wood and insulation to be installed should be made with your contractor prior to your preparing your own estimate.

The stud wall's bottom board (the one sitting on the ground to which the 2 × 4s are attached) is called the sill plate. The top board is called the top plate. Fire breaks are cut from 2 × 4s and are installed horizontally between the studs at the height of the insulation. Fire breaks aid in holding up the top half of the wall's insulation. The stud wall is constructed on the floor and raised up against the block or concrete wall and secured with masonry fasteners to the floor and walls and fastened to the floor joists above.

If the basement is to be finished, interior walls and room partition walls will need to be constructed. The partition walls are also constructed from 2 × 4s, 16 in. apart and raised when completed. The sill is anchored to the concrete and the top plate is fastened to the floor joist above.

- Install the electrical and plumbing: The basement's electrical and plumbing are installed prior to hanging the insulation and drywall. Electrical and plumbing will be reviewed later in separate sections in this chapter.
- Install baton fiberglass basement insulation between 2 × 4 studs.
- Staple on the vapor barrier (clear plastic sheathing).
- Hang the drywall: Drywall is also referred to as Sheetrock. After the drywall is fastened to the stud wall, the seams and corners are covered with metal strips. The metal strips are then covered with drywall tape and several layers of plaster (or "mud" or "mucking") are applied on top of the tape. Usually two to three coats of mud are applied and sanded between applications. Primer and paint are then applied to complete the wall.
- Install baseboards and door and window trim.

## BASEMENT CEILING

The primary purpose of a basement ceiling is to support the load of the first floor. The support required will vary according to the size and load (weight) of the first floor and should be detailed in the architectural drawings. Support is not complicated and costly; support simply means doubled 2 × 10s or an extra jack post here and there. The basic components to the basement ceiling vary little from one project to the next.

○ Install the mudsill: A construction word for a wooden ledge that sits on top of the cinder block/concrete wall. The ledge is anchored to the concrete. The mudsill provides a flat, smooth surface for the first storey joists to sit on.
○ Construct the joists: The ceiling joists of one storey are the floor joists of the next storey. Joists are typically spaced 16 in. apart; however, the spacing can vary depending on the board size of the joists. Generally, the larger the board (for example, 2 × 10 versus 2 × 8), the greater the spacing. Joists are installed along the entire length or width of the ceiling. Usually the joists are installed in the same direction on all the floors above.

　　Some contractors install a product called TJI or engineered lumber as opposed to the natural 2 in. wide wood board. The product is slightly more expensive; however, TJI comes with guarantees such as squeak resistance.

　　In between the joists, a bridge is installed to stabilize the joists. The bridges look like cross bars installed every 6 ft. running the length of the joists.
○ Build support: If the joists run for too long without an extra support board, partition support wall or jack post, the weight from the floor above will collapse the basement ceiling. Your architect or contractor will inform you about where reinforcement is required.
○ Complete the ductwork, electrical and plumbing: If ducts or plumbing travel across the ceiling in a basement that is planned to be finished with drywall, a box frame constructed from 2 × 2 boards will be built around the protruding materials.

○ Finish the ceiling: A hung/suspended ceiling is a simple option for a basement. Wire hangars, attached to the joists, hold up the crossties (or some refer to it as ceiling grid). The ceiling sits into the grid. Another option is drywall. The drywall is secured to the joists, metal strips, taped, mudded, sanded, primed and painted.

○ Backfill around the basement walls: Local building codes and your contractor's schedule determine when gravel and soil will be filled around the basement foundation walls. Utilizing the existing excavated soil that has been stored on site is frequently sufficient; however, additional soil/gravel may be required to build up along the sides of the house to prevent water from pooling next to the basement walls. This process is referred to as grading.

## BASEMENT STAIRS

○ Create an opening: Decide how large you would like your stairway opening to be since expanding later is expensive. Saw out an opening in the basement ceiling joists. Then 2 × 4s are fastened to the joists for reinforcement at the square opening.

○ Determine the number of stairs: Your contractor will calculate the length of the diagonal using construction tables. Tables provide the number of stairs required for your total rise (vertical height from the floor to top of the stairs) and the run (the horizontal length from the top first step to the bottom step measured along the floor lcvcl). The contractor will figure out the number of steps based on local codes with a specific tread depth (part you step on) and riser height.

○ Install the stringer: Stringers are usually 2 × 12s (refer to architectural plans to confirm planned board size) installed on either side of the opening from the ceiling down to the floor. The stringer becomes the frame for your stairs. Right angles for the risers and treads are sawed into the stringer. The stringer is attached to the ceiling joists with an angle bracket (large steel staple) and to the concrete floor with masonry fasteners.

○ Attach the treads and risers: The treads are usually constructed from round-nosed tread stock and hammered onto the stringers. The risers are generally cut from 3/4 in. plywood.

○ Finish the stairs: Finish with the material of your choice and attach a railing with posts spaced 4 in. apart, measured from the center of each post (building codes vary).

NOTE: Stairways that end in a platform, turn and continue in another direction require slight construction alterations. Your contractor will construct a simple platform with 2 × 4s topped with 3/4 in. plywood. The diagonal or length of the stringer will be recalculated.

## THE FIRST STOREY

### FLOORS

Generally, all floors are identical in construction. All floors, including backsplits, sidesplits, two storeys and bungalows, require floor joists, plywood, vapor barrier and a floor finish. With two-storey structures, the first floor rests on the ceiling joists of the basement below and the second floor sits on the ceiling joists of the first floor.

○ Install the subfloor: Apply adhesive (glue) to top of the basement ceiling joists or first-floor joists. Nail 3/4 in., 4 × 8 plywood sheets to the floor joists.

○ Install the underlayment (optional): An underlayment can be installed on top of the subfloor and is made of 1/4 in. underlayment plywood.

○ Lay a vapor barrier: Plastic sheathing improves moisture resistance, though simple paper sheathing can be used.

○ Finish the floor: Hardwood can be applied directly on top of the vapor or paper barrier. Tile, either ceramic or stone, requires additional layers:

- Spread thin-set mortar on the plywood subfloor.
- Fasten standard 32 sq. ft. cementboard/backerboard to the subfloor.
- Trowel on another layer of thin-set mortar: Mortar is spread using a trowel to create furrows. When complete, the mortar will look as though it's been applied with a comb.

## Framing and Finishing Walls, Ceiling and Roof

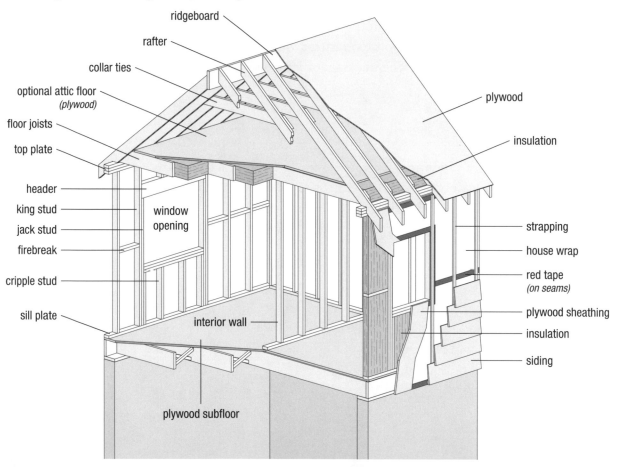

- Lay down tiles.
- Spread grout on top of entire area and wipe the tiles clean.
- For a laminate floor, the sheet or tiles are applied directly onto the plywood subfloor with adhesive.

## FIRST STOREY WALLS

○ Build the stud-frame wall: The construction of the first-floor stud walls is similar to the basement stud walls. Completed on the floor and raised, the stud walls are built to accommodate for door openings, windows and fireplaces. Within a stud wall, extra reinforcement for load, openings and fire breaks is required. Fancy terms such as king studs, trimmers, cripples, jacks, headers, bottom/sole/sill and top plate are used to describe extra 2 × 4s installed here or there to reinforce the stud wall. Of primary concern to you are the size and number of boards, and the number of labor hours required to construct the walls.

○ Secure the stud frame to the subfloor.

○ Install electrical, plumbing and ductwork: Metal plates are attached to any 2 × 4s that have wires or plumbing running through them in order to protect against accidental drilling or hammering.

○ Fill with baton insulation and attach a vapor barrier (plastic sheathing).

○ Hang drywall; apply metal strips, tape, mud, sand, prime and paint.

○ Finish the outside first-floor walls
  - Install sheathing: Sheathing is usually 1/2 in., 4 × 8 plywood sheets (coded CDX) hammered onto the outside studs. Refer to local building codes and discuss with your

contractor the standard plywood width or alternative sheathing options. Sheathing overlaps the basement foundation wall by 1/2 in. or more.

- Cut window and door openings from the inside of the house.
- Install rigid board insulation on top of the sheathing (optional): To improve R-values, a layer of rigid insulation can be installed on top of the plywood sheathing.
- Install a vapor barrier: House wrap or Typar/Tyvec (similar to opaque Saran Wrap) is installed on top of the plywood or insulation.
- Apply red tape on all house-wrap seams.
- Install exterior finish.

## EXTERIOR FINISH

*Siding (Vinyl or Wood)*
- Nail 1 in. width boards spaced every 24 in. on the house wrap to create an air space. This is referred to as strapping.
- Attach the siding to the 1 in. boards.

*Brick or Stone*
- Cut real stone on site to fit the wall pattern. Cultured stone does not require on-site cutting.
- Lay the bricks, real stone or cultured stone on top of the house wrap leaving an air space between the house and the material being laid. The bottom layer sits on the foundation wall.

*Stucco*
- Attach a metal wire sheet to the house wrap.
- Apply a layer of plaster and dry.
- Apply two more layers, with the final layer premixed with paint color.

NOTE: Several methods of stucco application are available. For example, another popular method is to fasten sheets of rigid polystyrene insulation on top of the house wrap instead of the metal wire sheets. Three layers of plaster are then applied on top of the insulation. Discuss application options with your contractor. Ensure you understand the materials to be used in order for you to produce your own cost estimate.

# FIRST FLOOR CEILING/SECOND FLOOR

The structure of the first floor ceiling and the second floor walls is identical to the structure of the basement ceiling and first floor walls. The floor and wall materials used and the pattern of construction are repeated until all the storeys have been completed. The floor materials are the same, including joists, bridges, adhesive, subfloor and finish.

The second floor walls are built as the first floor with stud frames constructed on the floor, raised and insulated. The vapor barrier is applied and the drywall is hung. Outside, plywood sheathing, house wrap and the exterior finish are installed.

Knowing that labor and structural materials required to construct the floors and ceilings of one storey are repeated for the second floor (and third floor if required) helps to simplify house construction.

## THE ROOF

The contractor may try to engage you in a potentially complicated and confusing discussion of various roof designs that incorporates run, rise and slope. A comprehensive understanding of roof construction is not required to participate in discussions and to produce your own cost estimate. Further, as long as the design is esthetically pleasing, let the architect worry about the measurements and let the contractor work out the minor construction adjustments to add reinforcement. The final measurements may be unique; however, the basic construction of a roof is similar from one project to the next.

**Standard Trussed Roof**

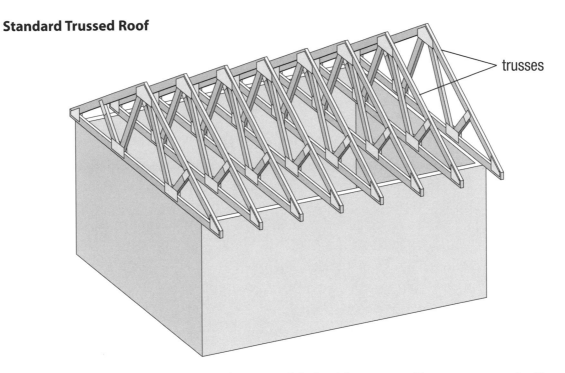

trusses

A roof can contain an attic or be assembled with trusses. Trusses are typically used on top of a protruding garage or shed if the plan is not to finish the attic space. Trusses arrive as prefabricated or "prefab" triangular sections that require a crane to lift. Trusses are secured to the top storey ceiling joists. The two-dimensional trusses are installed, domino style, until a three-dimensional roof is completed. Once assembled, the steps to finish the roof are identical to a roof constructed from scratch.

Trusses can be costly; however, the expense can be evaluated against the labor and materials costs to build new. Chapter 7 will provide insight to evaluate the cost differential.

## *Standard Roof Construction with an Attic*

- Lay insulation and 3/4 in. plywood sheathing on the attic floor. Insulation between the floor joists should be installed prior to laying down plywood. If the plan is to leave the attic floor unfinished, the insulation will be installed after the roof is completed.

- Install the ridge board: A roof is shaped in the form of a triangle. The ridge boards (or ridge beams) run along the length of the peak. The size of the lumber required for the ridge board will be noted on the architectural plans, but as an example, the architect might install two 2 × 12s strung together. The purpose of the ridge board is to have something for the sides to fasten to. The ridge board is held up by wood braces that are attached or "cleated" to the plywood floor.

- Install rafters: The rafters create the sides or slope of the roof. The architectural plans will determine the size of boards to be installed, but as an example, the contractor may use 2 × 8s installed 16 in. apart. The rafters are fastened to the ridge board and are cut to fit against and fasten to the attic floor joists. Once attached to the floor joists, the rafters will hang out over the side of your house.

- Install collar ties: Collar ties are horizontal support beams that are fastened up into the roof rafters to prevent the roof from sagging or possibly collapsing. The number of collar ties required will be dictated by the architectural plans. Visually, from the inside, once installed, the collar ties appear to cut off the peak of the roof. If the attic is to be finished, drywall is usually attached to the collar ties, effectively flattening the cathedral.

- Install outriggers: Outriggers are necessary to finish the roof from the outside and to prepare for the installation of the soffits. Outriggers, constructed from 2 × 4s, are cut to fit the overhang space between the bottom tip of every roof rafter and the exterior wall around the entire house.

- Attach the last rafters: Roof rafters are installed to the ridge board and to the ceiling joists. The rafters provide an overhang along the side of the house to which outriggers can be attached. However, on the ends of the house that do not have the protruding rafters, an overhang is created by attaching 2 ft. long outriggers, spaced 16 in. apart,

## Typical Roof Framing and Finishing

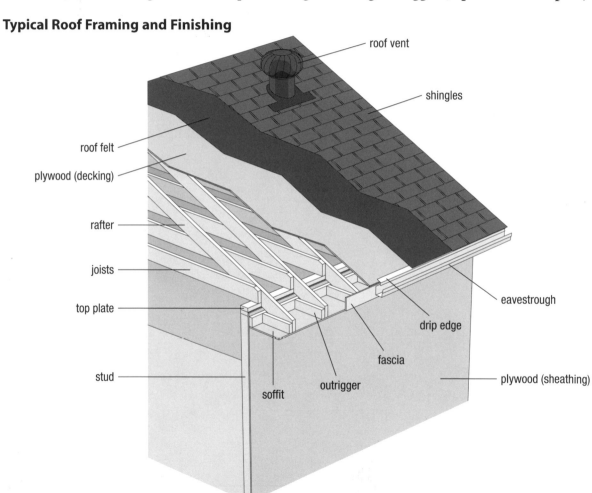

perpendicular to the existing roof rafters. The final rafters, or barge rafters, can be fastened to the outriggers to finish off the overhang.

○ Lay roof sheathing and prepare for shingles: The roof sheathing or 1/2 in., 4 × 8 plywood sheets (refer to architectural plans and discuss with your contractor the width of plywood or alternative materials) are fastened to the rafters. Metal flashing is installed on top of the plywood to protect against water damage near the chimney or where the roof may butt against a vertical wall. Flashing is made of corrosion-resistant aluminum and is commonly L-shaped. Terms such as step flashing (overlapping) and upper and lower apron around the chimney are simply fancy names used to describe the shape and location of flashing.

○ A drip edge (molded metal strip) is installed along the edge of the entire perimeter of the roof to direct the water into the eves (gutter), preventing water from dribbling down onto the fascia.

○ Lay roof felt and ventilation material: Asphalt-impregnated roof felt (feels like lightweight black felt) comes in rolls and is nailed on top of the sheathing. For ventilation along the peak of the ridge board, a layer of ridge vent (looks like thick, black plastic hair netting) is laid down running the entire length of the beam. To further enhance ventilation, a roof vent called a "Big Whirly" made of aluminum or galvanized tin is installed.

○ Lay shingles: Shingles are laid on top of the roof felt.

○ Install wiring and plumbing: If the plan is to finish the interior of the attic, then wiring for fixtures, outlets and plumbing should be installed prior to insulating.

○ Insulate attic interior: Attic insulation is installed between the rafters; however, to enhance ventilation, insulation should not be stuffed into the overhang. To hold up the insulation and as an added vapor barrier, plastic sheathing can be stapled on top of the roof insulation.

○ Finish the attic interior: If desired, drywall can be hung over the plastic sheathing.

○ Finish drywall with metal corner strips, mud, sand, prime and paint.

○ Install soffits, eves and fascia: The soffit covers the underside or the outriggers of the roof. The soffit has ventilation holes to prevent moisture buildup in the attic. The purpose of the eves is to carry rainwater along the perimeter of your house to the downspout ending underground away from the house (refer to local building codes). Finally, the fascia is a flat, but finished decorative trim that is fastened to the butt ends of the rafters.

## ELECTRICAL

Labor is your largest electrical expense. A certified electrician connects all lighting fixtures and outlets to the breaker panel. Highways of wires run from the service entrance panel or SEP (also referred to as the distribution center, breaker panel or fuse box), often in the basement, to each floor and to the outside. Connecting and running wires is not complex; however, since an electric current is continuous, a faulty broken wire, loose or exposed connection or incorrect installation can be disastrous. Hiring a certified or professional electrician is required to keep you safe, to pass necessary building inspections and to help support an insurance claim in the unlikely event of an electrical fire.

Electrical materials are not as costly as other structural items the contractor is responsible for obtaining. Major structural materials, which can include a breaker box (averages $200), a few bolts of various-sized wires ($30 for 500-foot bolt) and miscellaneous receptacles (average $1 each). Finishing materials that you are responsible for include the lighting fixtures and dimmer switches. Fixtures and dimmers can be costly, yet you have price and purchase control.

○ Confirm set-up fees with the utility company: Frequently, the utility company in your local area installs the cable from the street line to the house. Call your utility company for fees. Further, a meter that records the consumption is installed along the side of an exterior wall.

○ Install the breaker panel and connect the outside cable: Most new homes or major renovations require a 200-amp panel or higher. A 200-amp panel has more breaker switches than the 100-amp. Years ago, a 100-amp panel was sufficient to meet our electrical needs. However, as time has passed, such items as wall ovens, air conditioning, hot tubs, big-screen TVs and halogen lights have increased the electrical load on a house and, by extension, the number of breaker switches required on a panel. An

## Typical Electrical System

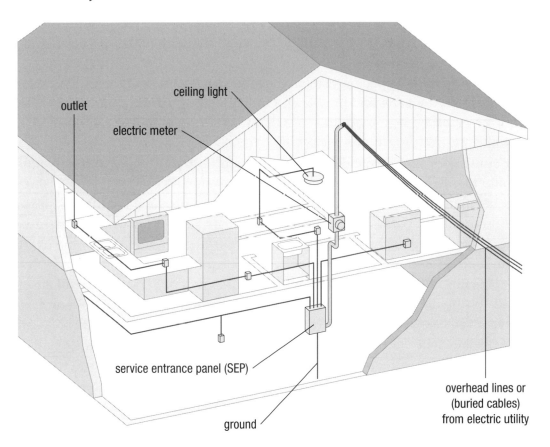

outlet

ceiling light

electric meter

service entrance panel (SEP)

ground

overhead lines or
(buried cables)
from electric utility

electrical assessment will be made early on to determine the size of panel needed. For smaller renovations that involve adding a few extra pot lights here or there, the panel may not need to be upgraded if extra, unused breaker switches are available.

○ Connect wires to the breaker panel and run to outlets/fixtures: Various sizes of wires connect to your panel, travel around your house and end at desired locations. Your architect will prepare a wire map for the electrician to follow. For smaller renovations, the electrician will determine how to tap into your electrical system within the room or may need to figure out how to run the wires all the way down to your panel to connect to another breaker.

○ All appliances require a specific size (or gauge) of wire to handle the electrical load (gauge codes vary by state and province). Ceiling lighting fixtures and receptacles/outlets require 14.2 or 14.3 gauge wire; they are the most common and are purchased in 500 ft. bolts. Thicker, more expensive wires (for example, 8.3 or 10.3 gauge) are necessary for appliances that demand more power, such as dryers, ovens and air conditioners, and should be invoiced by the yard. For your own general cost calculations (you can cost out the above wire gauge examples), you can multiply the length needed by the price of the required wire. Consider using these wire gauges for your initial cost estimate. Later on, you should research within your local area to determine exact gauge. Ask your contractor about the codes for your local area.

○ Your electrician may try to engage you in a confusing conversation about installation obstacles. Problems are usually centered on the connection of wires. Your architect may have already completed electrical diagrams; however, for smaller renovations, your electrician will operate independently. Since wires are fairly limited and inexpensive, try not to feel pressured into participating in problem solving. Your responsibility is to estimate the size and quantity of wires and the required number of labor hours. Let the contractor worry about how to install, for example, a three-way dimmer switch—you have already factored the materials and labor into your estimate equations.

○ Install the fixtures, receptacles and covers: You should select the halogen lights. A variety of styles and price points are available and since quantities are usually large, attention should be paid to value. For example, new homes may require 60 or more halogen lights. At a minimum of $30 per light (excluding light bulbs, switches and insulating boxes), the total cost can quickly exceed $1,800.

A halogen light includes the housing (a hollow pot that fits up into the ceiling) and the trim (the decorative molding that fastens into the housing and surrounds the light bulb).

The housing and trim are usually purchased as one kit and can be reasonably purchased at around $30. If the housing is installed into an insulated ceiling (that is, a top floor ceiling with the attic above), electrical codes require the installation of a metal box that surrounds the housing in the attic. The box is necessary to keep the bulb heat away from the insulation. A box can be purchased separately for about $20.

○ As a final note, your contractor may recommend installing transformers. A transformer sits in the housing beside the halogen light for the sole purpose of reducing the voltage or light intensity. Quite frankly, a standard halogen light with a regular dimmer switch lowers the brightness of the bulb and accomplishes the same effect at a fraction of the price. Transformers are expensive to purchase, have a limited life span, are difficult to replace and require expensive low-voltage dimmer switches. A $1,800 expense can easily mount to over $4,000 with transformers.

## PLUMBING

Your plumber is required to bring the water in, drain it out and run an occasional air vent to the roof to discharge the smell of dirty water. Similar to electrical, the installation of plumbing is fairly straightforward; however, plumbing should also be installed by a certi-

## Typical Plumbing System

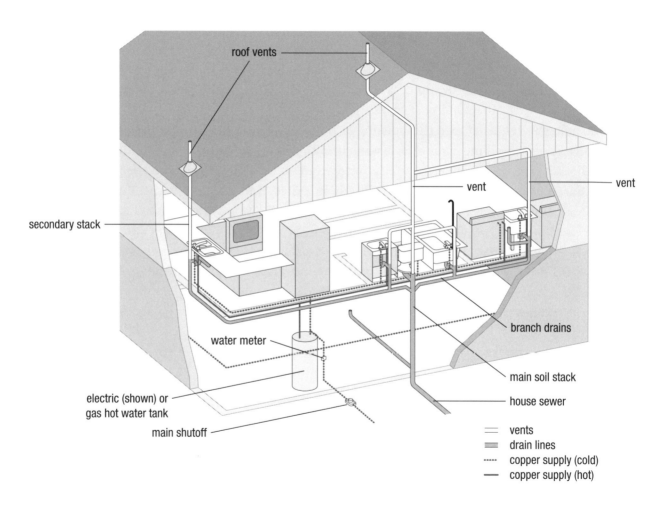

fied professional. Improperly installed plumbing, although not as life threatening as electrical, can cause a tremendous amount of property damage.

Similar to electrical, structural materials costs are insignificant compared with the labor charge for installation. For the construction of a new home, the total cost of piping can be considered an insignificant percentage of the total construction cost. Don't become overwhelmed with fancy explanations and materials descriptions. A 10-foot-long, 4-inch ABS/PVC drain pipe costs only $10! Considering average height from the foundation to the top-floor drain is approximately 25 feet, 20 to 30 10-foot pipes cost out at $200 to $300, which covers most of your drain materials. Costs for hot-and-cold water supply copper pipes that run in parallel throughout your house are also reasonable. For small bathroom or kitchen renovations, your plumber will connect to the existing system. The materials cost for two little copper pipes to "T" from the existing plumbing is pennies. Granted, the labor involved can be extensive, but invoices for structural materials should be realistic.

Put aside confusing explanations from those with impressive professional titles and focus on what size pipes are required to bring the water in and drain it out. Most of the potentially confusing design work and discussion of how best to deliver water up to the top storey and to the various areas of the house and to drain away to the city sewer will be determined by the architectural plans or by your plumber/contractor.

Common structural materials include a hot-water tank, copper supply pipes and ABS or PVC drain pipes. Older homes have cast iron drain pipes. Today, cast iron has been replaced with tough plastic, referred to as ABS (acrylonitrile butadiene styrene), or PVC (polyvinyl chloride). ABS is used in above-ground or in-house drain pipes while PVC is used for underground drain pipes. Some states and provinces have banned ABS, and PVC is used exclusively. Check local building codes and confirm with your architect or contractor.

For those who are renovating an older home, ABS or PVC pipes can be connected to an existing cast iron pipe with "no hub" connectors (a fancy name for a connection system made of a neoprene sleeve that wraps around the point of connection and the stainless steel clamps that hold it in place). The plumber should pay careful attention when drilling into a cast iron pipe to avoid shattering. However, a replacement 3-inch 10-foot PVC pipe averages around $1 per foot. To keep your labor rate down, if you are available, help the plumber remove the pipe and watch as the pipe is put in and the drain lines are attached to it.

○ Confirm set up fees with the utility company: A main city water line is located underground and runs along the street. The utility company will shut off this line to allow for a house connection. The city or your plumber will install a 3/4 in. copper pipe connecting line (size varies, check local building codes or plans) that runs underground from the street to your house.

○ Install a hot water tank: Hot water tanks are usually gas heated (and sometimes electric) and require a gas line to the tank and a vent that removes the carbon monoxide generated from the flame to the outside. You will need to decide whether to rent a tank from the gas company or to purchase the unit (check with your gas company); however, a gas professional is required to install the gas line and the outside vent.

○ The water line from the outside runs into the house and splits or "Ts" into two lines—one copper line for the cold and one copper line directing the water into, through and out of the hot-water tank.

○ Run side-by-side hot and cold 3/4 in. copper pipes to each faucet: Hot and cold copper pipes run in parallel (not touching each other) along the basement ceiling and up through the entire house to every faucet. The hot and cold copper pipe is usually surrounded by insulation when running along the basement ceiling.

○ Install ABS or PVC drain lines: Once the plumbing has been connected to bring the water in, your plumber will also be working on removing the wastewater. All your drainage pipes for toilets, sinks, bathtubs and laundry tubs are eventually connected down to the main drainage pipe. To drain water, 2 in. ABS or PVC pipes (toilets use 3 in. pipe) are installed to every drain in the house. These 2 in. drain pipes run down to one main 3 in. ABS or PVC drain line. The main drain line runs to the street and connects to the main city sewer line unless the sewage runs to a septic tank.

One or more air vent pipes are attached to the main 3 in. drain pipe and run up through the roof to vent unpleasant odors and keep the sewage flowing. After all the piping is installed, you are faced with the fun, yet costly, venture to the fixture and bathroom store.

# FURNACE/AIR CONDITIONING

An engineer will determine, based upon square footage, the size of furnace and air conditioner that are required to adequately heat and cool a new home or a large addition. For smaller renovations, the existing system may be sufficient or an alternative heat source, such as baseboard heaters, may be recommended.

A new furnace or air conditioner is a large, unavoidable, lump sum cost. An evaluation of price points and quality is required, particularly if your contractor is directing you to a preferred supplier. Understanding how the furnace and air conditioning innards operate is not as necessary as knowing what materials and labor your contractor is responsible for.

Air travels in a circular pattern in your house. Old air is drawn into the furnace from your house, heated or cooled and filtered, and new air is pumped out. Your contractor's job is to install air intake/cold air return ducts that draw air from various wall/floor vents to the furnace and outtake ducts that push air from the furnace back out to the floor vents. Your

## Typical Heating and Cooling System

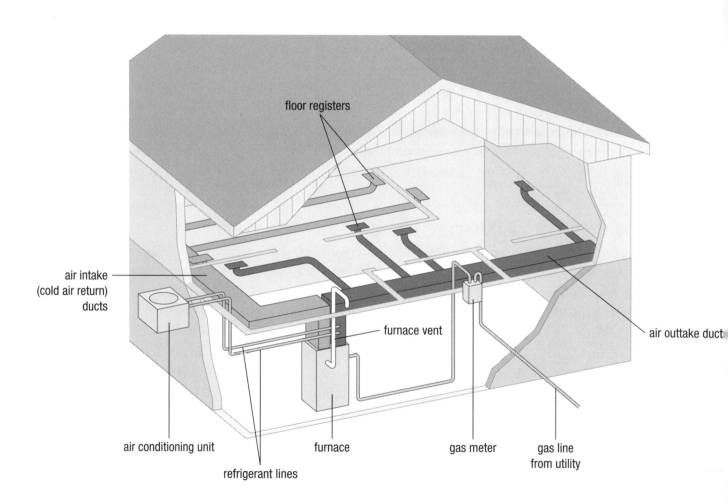

floor registers

air intake
(cold air return)
ducts

furnace vent

air outtake duct

air conditioning unit

furnace

gas meter

gas line
from utility

refrigerant lines

contractor is responsible for purchasing the galvanized tin ducts that can come in a variety of duct shapes and sizes with fancy names such as round pipe, elbows and stacks to assist in connecting to desired locations.

Once ducts are installed, a vent is installed to remove the carbon monoxide generated from the furnace gas flame to the outside. The air vent can run outside via the chimney or through the closest outside wall. The utility company is usually responsible for the proper installation of the furnace and vents. The air conditioner is also installed by a professional. Without too much detail, the unit utilizes the evaporation of a refrigerant, like Freon gas, to cool warm air inside the house. The Freon travels from the air conditioner to the furnace and recycles back to the air conditioner.

## FIREPLACE

Due to building costs and to poor energy efficiency, traditional handmade wood-burning mason fireplaces are quickly being replaced with prebuilt gas or wood-burning hearths that sit in a stud frame and vent up to the roof either horizontally or vertically through an exterior wall.

### Wood

To install a fireplace, your contractor needs to build a wood frame constructed from 2 × 4s to set the unit in. The hearth slides into the frame and a vent is attached. The vent pipe, made of galvanized metal, is attached to a hole in the top of the hearth. An end cap is placed on the top of the vent.

From the interior, heat-resistant drywall is installed on top of the wood frame, painted and framed. If you prefer stone or brick, a mason will install this on top of the drywall. On the exterior, a box frame can be built around the protruding roof vent. To keep costs down, many pipes are left unfinished and are barely noticed from the street.

**Framing of Fireplace Insert**

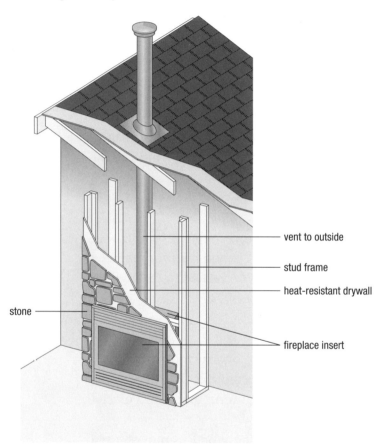

stone

vent to outside

stud frame

heat-resistant drywall

fireplace insert

### *Gas*

Gas fireplaces are installed in a similar way, with a frame, heat-resistant drywall and a vent. With gas, you have a choice of either running the vent vertically through the roof or, if the fireplace sits on an exterior wall, running the vent out horizontally through the wall to the outside. The gas line is tapped from the existing gas furnace line. Materials costs to connect the fireplace are very small; however, you will need to hire a gas professional to ensure the line is without leaks and is installed to code.

## WINDOWS

Ensure your contractor follows the window manufacturer's installation instructions to guarantee manufacturer's warranties. There are slight variations between window companies, and many manufacturers prefer that you employ their own installers to ensure the installation is completed as per their specifications. For your own cost estimate, slight variations will have little impact on your calculations. Naturally, the windows are the most expensive percentage of your window installation cost. Extra caulking or insulation here or there has little impact.

To avoid breakage, windows are typically installed after the roof and wall sheathing (plywood) have been installed. Openings should have already been cut and felt paper should frame the window on the outside. A bead of caulking is applied around the frame and the window is inserted. A window is secured to the outside wall with a flange—a metal "L" strip—that is attached to the window and nailed to the wall exterior. The flange is sealed with caulking and tape to prevent water from seeping in. From the interior, wood shims—small pieces of wood—are jammed between the stud frame and the window for leveling. Insulation is loosely inserted between the stud frame and the window, but a 1-inch air space is left and filled with foam tube insulation.

When your windows arrive, a very careful inspection should be done to ensure they are free of cracks, scratches (on both the frame and the panes), dents and malfunctions. Ensure the sizes are correct and all the parts for installation have arrived.

Congratulations! You now have a basic understanding of construction that will provide you with a definite advantage when delegating and negotiating with your contractor. No matter what the field, managing and delegating is difficult, if not impossible, without an understanding of the tasks required to successfully complete the project. Now you are equipped with such an understanding and can more confidently work your way around a jobsite and effectively participate and problem solve with your tradespeople. Knowing just the basics of construction and having an appreciation for the tradespeople's tasks ahead can go a long way in the development of a successful relationship with your contractor.

In the next chapter, the most significant question of any renovation project will be answered—how much will your project cost? The fun is about to begin as you move ahead to chapter 7, Calculating Your Own Cost Estimate.

# 7 Calculating Your Own Cost Estimate

*"The outhouse is only temporary until we're back on budget."*

- - - - - - - - - - - -

To evaluate the accuracy of your contractor's quote and to effectively negotiate a contract, you need to have an idea of structural materials costs and of the labor required to complete your project. Without preparing your own estimate, you will have difficulty assessing whether a contractor has lowballed an estimate to win the business.

The practice of lowballing has been around for a long time and has been bad news for the industry as a whole. Contractors attempt to win business by producing a dishonest, underpriced quote, only to adjust invoices once the project has commenced. Actual project costs usually turn out to be the same as the other contractor's original estimates or, many times, are higher. Lowballing has been a source of frustration not only for homeowners, but also for reputable contractors. Reputable contractors get angry at those who produce lowball quotes. When homeowners mistakenly award contracts to underpriced estimates, the reputable contractor may be tempted to play the same lowball game with the next prospective client. The onus is on the homeowner to properly evaluate a quote, identify errors and award contracts to contractors who produce realistic estimates.

Before proceeding into pricing, below are several initiatives that can save you time, either in construction education or in the development of your own cost estimate:

1. Hire a construction consultant.
2. Cost only the top 10 structural materials.
3. Purchase a lumber take-off.

## HIRE A CONSTRUCTION CONSULTANT

Hiring a construction consultant is an option for those who are planning a large-scale new home renovation and are looking for ways to reduce the amount of time and worry spent on the project. The consultant, paid on average $150 an hour, manages the contractor and your construction project for you. The fee usually includes services such as preparing preliminary estimates, analyzing the contractor quote and invoices against the quote, ensuring the contractor builds as per the contract and maintaining project schedules. You can turn over the keys to the consultant and gain peace of mind that the project is in qualified hands.

*When home-owners mistakenly award contracts to underpriced estimates, the reputable contractor may be tempted to play the same lowball game with the next prospective client.*

You will need to invest some time in researching and managing the consultant. Ensure that the consultant will only be working for you and have only your best interests in mind. Consultants who have been around for some time will have developed strong, trusting relationships with several contractors. If you agree to hire one of the consultant's preferred contractors, you will need to assess whether the consultant is receiving financial incentives or kickbacks from the preferred contractors. Conflict of interest between you, the consultant and the contractor may occur. Since consultants are pricey, you should not be in the position of wondering whether the consultant has alternative interests.

Although $150 an hour seems expensive, the consultant is not on site all day. Depending on the project, the consultant may work anywhere from one to three hours per week. You can use the contractor's construction timeline to calculate the consultant's approximate fee. The dollar fee should be evaluated in terms of the percentage of your total project cost. When deciding whether to invest in a consultant, assess the fee in terms of the following:

✔ Do you have the time to manage the project? If an experienced consultant requires two to three hours a week, do you have at least that amount of time to devote?
✔ How much is your time worth?
✔ Is your project large enough that the consultant's fee will be offset by the identification of labor and materials savings?
✔ Is your project large enough to warrant an experienced on-site manager who will help foresee problems and minimize costly rework?

Consultants can be found in your local telephone directory or through your local home building store. The tricky part is to find a consultant who is willing to work on a residential home. Most consultants work on bigger commercial projects; however, by asking around, you may find residential companies, such as Renovation Management Company, or individuals in your area who are capable and willing to do the job and who want to make a little money on the side, for example, an employee behind the Pro Desk at Home Depot, a retired contractor or a friend who is an engineer.

## COST ONLY THE TOP 10 STRUCTURAL MATERIALS

The second suggestion is to calculate only the top 10 most expensive structural materials required for your job. Although preparing a detailed materials cost estimate will improve your understanding of the project and your negotiating abilities, completion of only a partial estimate of the structural materials will provide a starting point in determining whether the contractor's estimate is way off the mark. Table 7.1 ranks structural materials from highest to lowest cost for a 3,500-square-foot home, based upon U.S. retail pricing excluding tax and contractor markups. As a guide, Canadian residents can apply current exchange rates. Prices are for materials only. In order for you to evaluate a contractor's estimate, the labor to install both the structural and finishing materials should be calculated separately.

**Table 7.1   Top 10 Structural Materials Costs**

| STRUCTURAL MATERIALS | AVERAGE COST (USD) |
| --- | --- |
| 1. Concrete | $10,200 |
| 2. Lumber for plywood subfloor/plywood sheathing | 8,592 |
| 3. Insulation (basement, walls and roof) | 4,784 |
| 4. Lumber for joists, ties, rafters, ridge board, e.g., 2 × 8s | 4,613 |
| 5. Lumber for stud frame walls, e.g., 2 × 4s | 3,420 |
| 6. Drywall | 2,943 |
| 7. Paint and primer | 1,930 |
| 8. Gravel for foundation under concrete/backfill | 1,800 |
| 9. Lumber for floor plywood underlayment | 1,693 |
| 10. Cinder blocks (garage) | 1,350 |
| Total Top 10 Structural Materials Costs | $41,325 |

Lumber fluctuates with the current state of import/export supply. Over the past couple of years, the price of lumber has been increasing. It's hard to believe the price of a 4 × 8 plywood sheet has doubled in a year. Contractors, particularly large developers, are looking for and installing cheaper substitutes to lumber (see photo). After the brick is laid, a homeowner would not be able to see the difference. Confirm with your contractor what sheathing material has been priced within the estimate and watch to ensure the correct materials are installed.

*Typical Plywood Sheathing Substitute*

Despite price fluctuations, lumber will always be among the top 10 most expensive structural materials for new homes or major renovations due to the large quantities required. Over time, the order of the top 10 may vary, but the materials within the list should stay about the same. The total of $41,325 represents approximately 80% of all structural materials your contractor is responsible for purchasing.

For your interest, the top 10 finishing materials for a 3,500-square-foot home are listed in table 7.2.

**Table 7.2   Top 10 Finishing Materials Costs**

| FINISHING MATERIALS | AVERAGE COST (USD) |
|---|---|
| 1. Windows | $20,000 |
| 2. All flooring—hardwood/stone/tile/carpet | 19,300 |
| 3. All cupboards—kitchen, bathroom, basement | 16,300 |
| 4. Doors—garage, interior and exterior plus handles | 11,600 |
| 5. All exterior finishing materials—stucco, brick or stone | 7,000 |
| 6. Furnace | 5,000 |
| 7. Fireplace inserts—gas or wood-burning | 3,800 |
| 8. Lighting fixtures—box, trim, housing, dimmers, exterior | 3,700 |
| 9. Interior Trims—window and door casings | 3,300 |
| 10. Tubs—whirlpool, regular | 2,000 |
| Total Top 10 Finishing Materials Costs | $92,000 |

The total of $92,000 also represents approximately 80% of finishing materials costs. Medium- to high-end quality products have been used to estimate the above costs. The cost of finishing materials listed above depends on trade-offs within your personal budget.

Important to understand is that the structural materials your contractor is responsible for purchasing are significantly lower in cost than the finishing materials you select. Depending on the size of your project, the labor to install both structural and finishing materials constitutes a large percentage of a contractor's estimate.

When evaluating an estimate for a small renovation, such as a kitchen or bathroom, keep in mind that what you are evaluating is the labor cost for your project. For this type of renovation, most of the estimate is made up of finishing materials and labor. Since a structure is already in place, the quantity of structural materials such as 2 × 4s, drywall, electrical wire and pipes to connect or add to the existing structure is usually fairly small. The written layout of an estimate may be different from one contractor to the next, yet when the budgeted amount for finishing materials for a small renovation is stripped from your contractor's estimate, you should be able to effectively compare only the cost of labor between estimates.

## PURCHASE A TAKE-OFF

To even further simplify the costing process, consider purchasing a lumber take-off. Instead of spending the time calculating lumber requirements, a building supply store can estimate your lumber needs. Lumber is a significant cost for large-scale renovations and new home construction. For a new home, the entire frame, including the walls, floor and roof, are constructed from 2 × 4s, 2 × 6s, 2 × 8s, 2 × 10s, 2 × 12s and plywood. Lumber requires the greatest percentage of your time to calculate. With the assistance of this book, you can complete your own lumber calculations. However, you can save time and obtain a detailed lumber estimate by purchasing a take-off.

A lumber surveyor prepares a take-off using your architectural plans. The surveyor completes a detailed breakdown of required lumber quantities and associated costs. The take-off is so inclusive and accurate that the document could be used as a purchase order. Depending on your contractor's experience, a lumber surveyor may be employed for every project estimate.

To avoid paying for a take-off, ask the contractor if a lumber surveyor is employed and ask to see the take-off. If the contractor prepares the lumber estimate without a surveyor, you can purchase a take-off from either a local home building store (for example, from the Pro Desk at Home Depot) or a lumber mill. The fee for this service is approximately $150, but is free if the homeowner agrees to purchase the lumber from the retailer/mill. Although $150 sounds pricey, for a new home construction, $150 is a tiny fraction of the total lumber cost. Also, consider the amount in terms of the time you will spend calculating your own estimate. When speaking to the mill, mention that you are preparing an estimate for a large project. Avoid stating that you will be using the take-off to compare against a contractor's estimate. The mill may not wish to get involved.

It is important for you to size up the estimator to ensure that lumber quantities will not be intentionally over- or underestimated. A slight overestimation would cover waste; however, a large overestimation may be due to an estimator attempting to sell more lumber. On the flip side, an underestimation may be due to the estimator trying to lowball an estimate to win the business. The homeowner is required to evaluate and compare the take-off against the contractor's estimate to determine what is reasonable for the project. Mention to the contractor that, for the purposes of evaluation, you will require a breakdown of the total lumber estimate.

Purchasing a lumber take-off will save you an enormous amount of work, but you will need to go further in evaluating your contractor's full project estimate. Discussions around variances to your take-off will produce lumber results; however, other items within the quote need to be discussed. At a minimum, preparation of the remainder of the top 10 materials would be beneficial. If possible, try to complete a full cost estimate.

Whether you are preparing a top 10 or a full cost estimate, the actual process of preparing your own calculations will force you to think through project details prior to construction. Stressful last minute decisions of what and how much goes where will have been planned out. You will feel more confident in the daily operations of the project and in the negotiations with your contractor. The first step is to calculate the quantities of structural materials needed for your project. If you wish to calculate a full estimate, rather than a top 10 list, the formulas and average pricing can be found in appendix 2.

As you work through the following formulas and pricing for your own situation, you can study the example two-storey 3,500-square-foot home, on which these figures were based, in figure 7.1.

---

FIGURE 7.1    **Example of a 3,500 Sq. Ft. Home**

**Layout:**

Two storeys with a finished below-ground basement. Four bedrooms, three and one-half bathrooms. One wood and one gas fireplace. Hardwood throughout, except in the basement (carpet) and the kitchen and main entrance (tile).

**Structural Materials:**

Floor joists are constructed with 2 × 6s and 2 × 2 cross bridges and run widthwise from the front of the house to the back, measuring a length of 31 ft. Roof rafters are constructed with 2 × 8s with 2 × 8 collar ties centered every 17 ft. and spaced 16 in. apart. The ridge board is constructed with 2 × 10s. Standard 2 × 4s are used for all stud walls (including the basement), and cinder blocks are used for the foundation walls and the garage.

In order to begin your own cost estimate, you will require a clear picture of your project. Whether a small renovation or a large project, measurements need to be confirmed. For a large project, the architect's blueprints will supply detailed measurements. For a smaller renovation, measurements of every area of construction will need to be calculated.

Materials calculations are presented in U.S. imperial measurements. Although metric is used in Canada, most of the construction world in North America follows standard U.S. measurements. Most of the materials purchased and, generally, most of the discussions at local home building stores are in feet and yards. Employees at building supply stores can quickly convert measurements for you or you can refer to table 7.3 to calculate the most frequently used measurements including square feet, cubic square feet, cubic square yards and lineal feet. All of these measurements may seem daunting, but you will discover that you are using the same calculations over and over again since many materials are applied one on top of the other. The first few measurements take time but are convenient to use once you have them at your disposal.

## Table 7.3    Handy Reference for Measurements

**MEASUREMENTS**

LINEAL FEET – One dimensional. Use a tape measure to measure the length.

SQUARE FEET – Two dimensional. Measure the length and the width. Multiply the length and width to calculate square feet. Square feet = L × W.

CUBIC FEET – Three dimensional. Measure the length, width and depth in feet and multiply together. Cubic feet = L × W × H.

CUBIC YARDS – Three dimensional. Use cubic square feet and divide by 27. Cubic yards = Cubic feet ÷ 27.

**CONVERSION CHARTS**

U.S. Units to Metric Units

| From | Multiply by | Get |
|------|-------------|-----|
| Inches | 2.54 | centimeters |
| Feet | 0.3048 | meters |
| Yards | 0.9144 | meters |
| Square Feet | 0.0929 | square meters |
| Square Yards | 0.8361 | square meters |
| Cubic Feet | 0.0283 | cubic meters |
| Cubic Yards | 0.7646 | cubic meters |

Metric Units to U.S. Units

| From | Multiply by | Get |
|------|-------------|-----|
| centimeters | 0.3937 | inches |
| meters | 3.2808 | feet |
| meters | 1.0936 | yards |
| square meters | 10.764 | square feet |
| square meters | 1.1960 | square yards |
| cubic meters | 35.315 | cubic feet |
| cubic meters | 1.308 | cubic yards |

The next step is to confirm the lumber required for your project. Whether you or your estimator is preparing a lumber estimate, there needs to be a determination about what different-sized boards will be used for your project. You will have choices, but for the most part, your architect or contractor will follow construction standards and building codes. Determine from your architect or contractor the following information:

1. Are 2 × 4s or 2 × 6s planned for the stud walls?
2. What size are the floor joists: 2 × 8s, 2 × 10s or 2 × 12s? Will the joists be engineered wood or standard lumber board?
3. What size roof rafters and ridge boards are planned?

With this information, you or your estimator will be able to create an accurate lumber forecast. Try to encourage the estimator to do as much of the work for you as possible. Typically, the lumber surveyor details lumber only; however, if you have your take-off done at your local home building store, many times the store will be able to add to the take-off by completing the estimate for you for items such as insulation, plastic sheathing, drywall and tape. For a job that requires multiple materials such as electrical or plumbing, you may be required to leave your plans with one of the employees for a few days for the employee to produce an itemized materials quantity list. To save you time, try to have as much done as possible by someone else. Once completed, ensure that you have an understanding of the numbers, or else you won't be able to discuss with your contractor variances between it and your contractor's estimate.

For those of you who do not have the benefit of having a take-off done, you can easily calculate the big board items on your own. All of the materials formulas listed below *do not* take wastage into account. Wastage depends on a number of factors, including the design of your project and the contractor's and general tradespeople's/carpenter's attentiveness to utilizing and minimizing garbage. Since the formulas below do not account for waste, you will need to apply your judgment when assessing variances. A 10% variance isn't worth discussion, a 25% variance requires a detailed examination to uncover errors and a 50% difference is out of the question. With a 50%+ difference, your contractor is so far off the mark that a thorough explanation should be provided. Try to determine why the difference is so high—perhaps an honest mistake has been made in either your or your contractor's calculations. On the other hand, after

*At this stage, the benefit of having three contractor estimates becomes evident. You can compare and contrast the variety of calculations against what you have prepared to determine the most acceptable estimate.*

explanations have been provided, you may determine that your contractor was not accurately calculating your estimate. At this stage, the benefit of having three contractor estimates becomes evident. You can compare and contrast the variety of calculations against what you have prepared to determine the most acceptable estimate.

To begin your own rough cost estimate, the formulas for determining quantities and pricing for the top 10 most expensive structural materials have been listed below. Review your architectural or design plans and determine the structural materials that apply to your project. Apply the top 10 formulas and pricing listed below; in addition, you can refer to appendix 2 for formulas and pricing of all remaining structural materials.

## STRUCTURAL MATERIALS

### CONCRETE

In the house illustration, concrete will be utilized for the basement floor and walls, the garage floor, and footings.

The cubic yard calculation is:

$$\frac{\text{Height} \times \text{Width} \times \text{Depth}}{27}$$

Standard concrete depth for a basement floor is 4 inches (local codes vary by state and province).

For the basement wall width, confirm with your architect or contractor since width can vary, but for a quick calculation apply a standard 10 inches and divide by 12 to convert to feet (width: 10/12). Refer to your architectural plans for the wall height estimate, but ensure your calculations have taken into account that the basement walls sit approximately 2 feet above ground.

For footing width, allow 20 inches or approximately twice the width of the wall with a depth of 8/12 × total perimeter length (see architectural plans) divided by 27. All totals have been rounded up.

## ■ NUMBER OF CUBIC YARDS

| | |
|---|---:|
| Footings perimeter: 180 ft. length × 20/12 ft. width × 8/12 ft. depth = 200 cu. ft ÷ 27 | 8 |
| Basement Floor: 1,829 sq. ft. (length × width) × 4/12 ft. depth = 609 cu. ft. ÷ 27 | 23 |
| Basement wall: 180 ft. length × 11 ft. height × 10/12 ft. depth = 1,650 cu. ft. ÷ 27 | 62 |
| Garage footings: 80 ft. length × 20/12ft. width × 8/12 ft. depth = 89 cu. ft. ÷ 27 | 4 |
| Garage floor: 400 sq. ft. (length × width) × 4/12 ft. depth = 133 cu. ft. ÷ 27 | 5 |
| Total | 102 |
| Average cost per cu. yd. of ready-mix ($100 × 102) | $10,200 |

Since cement is delivered wet and ready to pour, extra cubic yards should be ordered to avoid running short. Discuss with your contractor the percentage guidelines applied, or call your local cement wholesaler or retailer (found in the phone book). A cement wholesaler can discuss the accuracy of your own calculations and will provide guidance about how much extra to order. Since cement can average around $100 per cubic yard, accuracy is important; you never want to find yourself short during the pour.

To lower your materials costs, consider constructing the foundation wall from cinder blocks (discuss with your contractor and check local building codes). One block covers .89 square feet and averages $2 a block. With the example basement wall measurements handy, a quick calculation illustrates that installing a block wall ($4,450) versus a concrete wall ($6,200) would save $1,750 in materials costs alone.

## LUMBER FOR SUBFLOOR AND SHEATHING (Plywood)

Three-quarter-inch plywood is installed on top of floor joists and on stairs and risers, and 1/2-inch plywood is used on the exterior walls and the surface of the entire roof. (Confirm board width with your contractor or refer to your architectural plans.) Both sheets are purchased in a 4 × 8 (32-square-foot) size. Calculate the total square-foot area and divide by 32 to determine the number of plywood boards:

$$\frac{\text{Total Plywood Square-Foot Area}}{32}$$

## 3/4-INCH 4 × 8 PLYWOOD SHEETS

### *Floors*

For simplicity, calculate the total square feet of one floor and multiply by the number of storeys, including the attic and finished basement floors. To refine your calculations, you could determine the square-foot area of each floor separately and add together—particularly for backsplit or sidesplit homes. **Note:** For this illustration, the basement subfloor will be constructed with Drycore that comes preassembled with 3/4-inch plywood. If you are planning on having the contractor build a subfloor from scratch, include the square footage within your total plywood calculations.

### *Stairs*

Plywood quantities will be fairly small; however, standard 4-foot-wide stairs (risers 7 inches, treads 10 inches) would require approximately one to two 4 × 8 sheets for every four to five stairs. If you are planning on a platform landing, one additional sheet should be factored in.

## ■ NUMBER OF 3/4-INCH 4 × 8 PLYWOOD SHEETS

| | |
|---|---:|
| Finished floors (excluding basement) sq. ft. | 3,150 |
| Stairs sq. ft. | 160 |
| Total sq. ft. | 3,310 |
| Number of 3/4 in. 4 × 8 boards (3,310 sq. ft. ÷ 32) | 104 |
| Average cost per board ($36 × 104) | $3,744 |

## 1/2-INCH PLYWOOD SHEETS

### *Walls*

For the outside exterior walls, you will need the height of your house from ground level to the attic floor. The square footage of all sides of your house should be calculated separately and added together.

### *Roof*

To calculate the square area of your roof, you require the length of the slope and the length of the roof. Your architectural plans should note the roof slope. If not, you will need to calculate. Draw a triangle on a piece of paper. The pitch or height of the triangle is A. The horizontal baseline is B (half the width of the house). The slope is C. (See figure 7.2).

**Figuring the Rise and the Run**

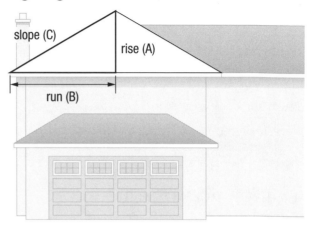

FIGURE 7.2    Slope

$$C = \sqrt{(A \times A) + (B \times B)}$$ (square root of A squared plus B squared)

Another method is simply to use a ruler and measure out the rise (A) and the run (B). Draw in the slope and measure it. To increase the accuracy of rise and run, your architect may have "5^12" written on your architectural plans beside the roof. Meaning: for every one-foot run, the rise goes up 5 inches.

After determining your roof slope, add 2 feet to the width of the slope and 4 feet to the length to account for overhang. NOTE: The 3,500-square-foot example home includes a front entrance overhang, and the square footage has been included in the plywood calculations below.

*Square footage of your roof:* (slope length × roof length) × 2 (to account for both sides of the roof)

Roof Square Area:

| | |
|---|---:|
| Standard [(slope 17 + 2 ft. overhang) × (38 + 4 ft. overhang)] × 2 | 1,596 |
| Cathedral  [(slope 14 + 2 ft. overhang) × (31 + 4 ft. overhang)] × 2 | 1,120 |
| Garage [(slope 12 + 2 ft. overhang) × (20 + 2 ft. overhang)] × 2 | 308 |
| Total | 3,024 |

## ■ NUMBER OF 1/2-INCH 4 × 8 PLYWOOD SHEETS

| | |
|---|---:|
| Exterior walls sq. ft. | 3,113 |
| Roof sq. ft. | 3,024 |
| Front entrance overhang sq. ft. | 304 |
| Total sq. ft. | 6,441 |
| Number of 1/2 in. 4 × 8 plywood sheets (6,441 ÷ 32) | 202 |
| Average cost per sheet ($24 × 202) | $4,848 |
| Total plywood cost ($3,744 + $4,848) | $8,592 |

## INSULATION

Building codes and your personal preferences will dictate the R-value insulation installed. The higher the R-value, the better the insulation and the lower the heating and cooling bills.

The square-foot coverage of each bag of insulation varies according to the R-value. If you would like to install better or inferior insulation than listed below, a chart with R-values and standard square-foot coverage of one bag can be found in appendix 1.

### R-31

Usually installed in the attic between the roof rafters and the attic floor joists. One R-31 bag covers 43 square feet. Refer to your roof calculations above and divide your roof square footage by 43 to determine the number of bags required.

### R-20

For 2 × 6 stud walls. One bag covers 49 square feet. Calculate square footage of all walls including both the finished and unfinished basement. Divide by 49 to determine the number of bags.

## R-12

For 2 × 4 stud walls. One bag covers 88 square feet. Determine total square footage including both the finished and unfinished basement and divide by 88.

### R-5 Extruded/Rigid Polystyrene

One and one-half-inch polystyrene is commonly installed in finished basement floors prior to pouring ready-mix (concrete) and in exterior basement walls and is occasionally fastened to exterior house walls on top of plywood sheathing. Polystyrene is also installed between basement sleeper studs instead of Drycore. One rigid board covers 32 square feet. Refer to your basement square-foot calculations and divide by 32 to determine the number of boards required.

   Any leftover insulation can be used around ducts and hot water pipes to keep the heat in.

## ■ NUMBER OF INSULATION BAGS

| | | |
|---|---|---|
| R-31, Attic (2,160 + 1,829 = 3,989 sq. ft. ÷ 43) | 93 | |
| Average cost per bag ($26.50 × 93) | | $2,462 |
| R-12, Exterior wall (4,320 sq. ft. ÷ 88) | 50 | |
| Average cost per bag ($20 × 50) | | $1,000 |
| R-5, Basement floor (1,829 sq. ft. ÷ 16) | 115 | |
| Average cost per bag ($11.50 × 115) | | $1,322 |
| Total Insulation Cost | | $4,784 |

## LUMBER FOR FLOOR JOISTS, DOOR HEADERS, RIDGE BOARD BRACE AND LUMBER FOR ROOF RAFTERS

### Floor Joists

Refer to your architectural plans to determine the board size planned for your floor joists. For this illustration, 2 × 6s with standard 16-inch spacing will be used in the calculations. For the example home and most with two-storey homes, the floors are usually the same length and width as the entire basement (finished and unfinished). As such, utilize the basement length and width measurements in the 3/4-inch plywood section.

For the length, average one 10-foot 2 × 6 board for every lineal foot. Divide the width by 10 to determine the number of 10-foot boards that are needed to fill the width. Multiply the length in lineal feet by the number of boards to cover the width. Multiply by the number of floors as follows:

[(Basement Length Lineal Feet × Basement Width Lineal Feet) ÷ 10 ft.] × # floors

For load support, an extra 2 × 6 support joist will be secured to various floor joists. If your plans do not yet indicate how many or where the support is needed, divide the above formula by 6 and add to the total to allow for an additional board every 6 lineal feet.

### Door and Window Headers

Refer to your plans to determine the size of boards for headers. Headers are located above door and window openings for reinforcement. Add the number of interior doors and exterior doors. To make life easy, multiply the total by 6 feet to allow for double headers. For windows, add up the lineal foot width of all windows and multiply by 2 to allow for double headers. Total doors and windows together and divide by the board length—10 feet—to estimate the number of 2 × 6 boards as follows:

(Number of door openings × 6 ft.) + (sum width of all windows × 2) ÷ 10 ft. boards

### Additional Areas Constructed from 2 × 6s

The example plan utilizes 2 × 6s as braces to support the standard roof ridge board. The braces sit perpendicular, every 10 feet, to the attic floor joists and attach to the roof ridge board. Calculate the length of the roof and divide by 10 feet to determine the number of 2 × 6 roof braces required.

### ■ NUMBER OF 2 × 6s

| | |
|---|---:|
| Floor joists (59 ft. length × 31 ft. width) ÷ 10 ft. × 2 floors | 366 |
| Add support joists (366 ÷ 6) | 61 |
| Door headers (32 door openings × 6 ft.) ÷ 10 ft. | 20 |
| Window headers (95 ft. window width × 2) ÷ 10 ft. | 19 |
| Roof ridge board brace (38 ft. length ÷ 10 ft.) | 4 |
| Total | 470 |
| Average cost per board ($5 × 470) | $2,350 |

### Roof Rafters

Refer to your architectural plans to determine the board size planned for roof rafters, collar ties and the ridge board. Standard sizes include 2 × 8s, 2 × 10s or 2 × 12s. If board sizes are not yet available, follow our illustration and apply 2 × 8s for the rafters and collar ties, and 2 × 10s for the ridge board. To calculate the number of boards needed for roof rafters, utilize measurements of the length of the slope and length of the roof as previously calculated.

To calculate the number of 2 × 8 boards, add 4 feet to the roof length to allow for a 2-foot overhang on either side. Estimate .75 boards per lineal foot to account for 16-inch spacing. To cover the slope, plan on 16-foot-long boards. If your slope is greater than 16 feet, longer boards should be purchased. In the example home, the slope measures 19 feet. In this case, 20-foot-long 2 × 8 boards will be installed.

$$(\text{Depth of roof} \times .75) \times 2$$

### Collar Ties

Collar ties are fastened to the rafters (every 16 inches) in the attic ceiling. Refer to your house plans to determine if collar ties are planned. For illustration, one 10-foot, 2 × 10 collar tie is secured to each roof rafter. The number of 2 × 10s will be the same as the number of rafters required to cover for the length of the roof.

### *Ridge Board*

The required number of 2 × 10s is determined from the roof length. They can be purchased in 20-foot boards. Divide the roof length by 20 feet to determine how many 10-foot 2 × 10s are required.

### ■ NUMBER OF 2 × 8s

Standard Roof:

| | | |
|---|---|---|
| Rafters: 42 lineal ft. × .75 × 2 sides (20 ft. boards) | 63 | |
| Collar Ties: 38 lineal ft. (10 ft. boards) | 38 | |
| Cathedral roof: | | |
| Rafters: 35 lineal ft. × .75 × 2 sides (20 ft. boards) | 53 | |
| Collar ties: 31 lineal ft. (10 ft. boards) | 31 | |
| Total 20 ft. boards | 116 | |
| Average cost per board ($14.70 × 116) | | $1,705 |
| Total 10 ft. boards | 69 | |
| Average cost per board ($6.90 × 69) | | $476 |

## ■ NUMBER OF 2 × 10s

Ridge board for standard and cathedral roofs:

(42 ft. roof length + 35 ft. roof length = 77 ÷ 20 ft.)                    4

    Average cost per board ($20.40 × 4)                                        $82

    Total cost for floor joists, ties, headers, ridge board, rafters          $4,613

## LUMBER FOR STUD FRAME WALLS (2 × 4s) (Includes Outriggers)

As discussed in chapter 5, a stud frame wall is built on the floor, raised up and secured to the floor. Calculate the total lineal feet for every wall in your house. A lineal foot is a one-dimensional measurement that requires a straight pull of the tape measure along the ground. Walls include exterior and interior partition walls, basement walls (most are finished with insulation and will need a stud frame), frames for closets and fireplaces. To determine the number of 2 × 4s for stud walls the formula is as follows:

    1.40  boards = 1 lineal foot

This formula includes lumber required for firebreaks between the studs.

### *Exterior Walls Lineal Feet*

To quickly measure the exterior walls, measure the total lineal feet around the perimeter of your house and multiply by the number of floors—don't forget to include the basement.

### *Interior Walls Lineal Feet*

Measure all interior walls. Don't worry about subtracting window and door openings since extra 2 × 4s for king jack and cripple studs will be required for reinforcement. Apply the above formula: 1.40 boards cover one lineal foot; however, if your ceilings are higher than

8 feet, increase the total calculations by the percentage height increase. For example, budgeting for a 10-foot ceiling, apply 1.75 boards per lineal foot as illustrated below:

$$\text{Number of 8 ft. 2} \times \text{4s per lineal foot} = 1.40 \times \frac{10 \text{ ft.}}{8 \text{ ft.}} = 1.75$$

If you have decided to build your stud walls from 2 × 6s, the quantity of 8-foot 2 × 6s is generally the same as the 2 × 4s. The difference is in the price. The amount of lumber required to cover the firebreaks between the 2 × 6s is 1.40 boards per lineal foot.

## Outriggers

Roof outriggers are also constructed from 2 × 4s. Convert the perimeter house lineal feet to inches by multiplying by 12. Divide by 16 since each outrigger is spaced 16 inches apart. Further, for a rough estimate divide by 4 since each outrigger is a standard 2 feet long and standard board length measures approximately 8 feet. The formula is as follows:

$$\frac{(\text{Perimeter Lineal Feet} \times 12/16)}{4}$$

## Sleeper Studs for Basement Floor

Drycore is planned for the finished basement floor in the illustration; however, if your contractor is building a subfloor from scratch, he or she will install 2 × 4 sleeper studs lying flat and spaced 16 inches apart. Measure the length of the basement and estimate one board for each lineal foot. Since 2 × 4s can be purchased in a variety of sizes, measure the basement floor width and divide by the length of the board (use 10 feet as an estimate). Multiply the number of boards needed for the width by the number of boards required for the length as follows:

$$\frac{\text{(Basement length lineal ft.)} \times \text{(Basement width lineal ft.)}}{10 \text{ ft.}}$$

## Additional Areas Constructed from 2 × 4s

In the example home, the front entrance overhang measures 38 feet in length and 8 feet in depth and is factored into the calculations below.

### STUD WALLS AND FRAMES 2 × 4s

| | |
|---|---:|
| Perimeter of house × 3 floors (180 lineal ft. × 3) × 1.40 | 756 |
| Interior walls (211 lineal ft. × 1.40) | 296 |
| Outriggers (2,160 lineal in. ÷ 16 = 135 ÷ 4) | 34 |
| Front entrance overhang (38 lineal ft. × 1.40) | 54 |
| Sleeper Studs | 0 |
| Total number of 2 × 4 boards | 1,140 |
| Average cost per board ($3 × 1,021) | $3,420 |

### DRYWALL

A 4 × 8 sheet of drywall covers 32 square feet. Add the total square footage of all finished walls and ceilings. Divide by 32 to determine the number of boards:

$$\frac{\text{Total Drywall Square-Foot Area}}{32}$$

## ■ NUMBER OF DRYWALL BOARDS

| | |
|---|---:|
| Finished interior walls sq. ft. | 6,000 |
| Finished ceilings sq. ft. | 4,458 |
| Total sq. ft. | 10,458 |
| Total number of drywall boards (10,458 ÷ 32) | 327 |
| Average cost per board ($9 × 327) | $2,943 |

### PAINT AND PRIMER

One gallon of paint covers approximately one coat of 400 square feet. One pail of primer covers 1,500 square feet. Determine the walls (total square foot area)—refer to drywall measurements and divide by coverage.

### GALLONS OF PAINT

| | | |
|---|---|---:|
| (10,458 sq. ft. ÷ 400) × 2 coats | 52 | |
| Average cost per gallon ($25 per gallon × 52) | | $1,300 |

### NUMBER OF PRIMER PAILS

| | | |
|---|---|---:|
| 10,458 sq. ft. ÷ 1500 | 7 | |
| Average cost per pail ($90 × 7) | | $630 |
| Total paint and primer cost | | $1,930 |

## GRAVEL

As with concrete, gravel is sold by the dimensional cubic yard. You will need 3/4-inch gravel under the concrete house and garage foundation and for drainage. Refer to your concrete measurements and calculate:

$$\frac{\text{Height} \times \text{Width} \times \text{Depth}}{27}$$

### Foundation

Standard gravel depth usually matches the thickness of the concrete—the standard 4 inches. To calculate your cubic-yard requirements, multiply the square footage of your basement by the fraction 4/12. For a 6-inch depth, multiply the square footage by 6/12. Divide by 27 to convert to cubic yards.

### Footings

Gravel is also required outside along the perimeter of your footings for drainage. Measure the lineal foot perimeter around your house, multiplied by standard 1-foot depth (check your local building codes or speak with your contractor) and divide by 27.

Later on, gravel will be required for your garage and driveway and an extra cubic yard should be ordered as fill on your yard at the exit point of an eves/downspout. The standard depth of gravel for your garage and driveway is 4 inches.

## ■ NUMBER OF GRAVEL CUBIC YARDS

| | |
|---|---:|
| Basement floor (1,829 sq. ft. × 4/12 = 609 cu. ft. ÷ 27) | 23 |
| Drainage around basement perimeter (180 cu. ft. ÷ 27) | 7 |
| Garage footings (80 ft. length × 20/12 width × 8/12 depth = 89 cu. ft. ÷ 27) | 4 |
| Garage floor (400 sq. ft. × 4/12 = 133 cu. ft. ÷ 27) | 5 |
| Driveway (800 sq. ft. × 4/12 = 267 cu. ft. ÷ 27) | 9 |
| Drainage for eves | 2 |
| Total cu. yd. | 50 |
| Average cost per cu. yd. ($36 × 50) | $1,800 |

## PLYWOOD UNDERLAYMENT

Underlayment is optional and is installed on top of 3/4-inch plywood subfloor. Underlayment can be purchased in 4 × 4 ft. (16 square feet) sheets. Use the above 3/4-inch plywood subfloor square-foot calculations subtracting rooms that will be finished with stone or ceramic. Divide by 16 to determine the number of 4 × 4 boards:

$$\frac{\text{Total Hardwood Square Feet}}{16}$$

## ■ NUMBER OF 1/4-INCH 4 × 4 UNDERLAYMENT BOARDS

| | |
|---|---:|
| Hardwood finished floor sq. ft. | 2,531 |
| Total number of 4 × 4 underlayment × 1/4 in. boards (2,531 ÷ 16) | 159 |
| Average cost per board ($10.70 × 159) | $1,693 |

## CINDER BLOCKS

In the example home, cinder blocks are planned for the construction of the garage. The garage measures approximately 20 × 20 feet; however, only three walls should be measured to allow for the garage opening. Standard garage wall height is 10 feet. Calculate the total square footage of all three walls and divide by .89 to determine the number of blocks needed. The formula for determining the number of cinder blocks is:

$$\frac{\text{Square Feet}}{.89}$$

## ■ NUMBER OF CINDER BLOCKS

| | |
|---|---:|
| Garage walls (20 × 10 ft.) × 3 walls = 600 sq. ft. ÷ .89 | 675 |
| Average cost per block ($2 × 675) | $1,350 |

# FINISHING MATERIALS

Finishing materials are usually more fun and much more interesting than structural materials yet usually more time consuming to research and purchase. Research of various recommended manufacturers and retailers is necessary in order to compare pricing. Information and assistance from the contractor can speed up the research process. Your contractor usually has preferred products and brands based upon positive installation and client experiences. You may be provided with a quality assessment of the brands you are interested in installing. For example, your contractor may have had previous construction difficulties or be aware of clients' dissatisfaction with a premium-priced brand.

Speaking from personal experience, I spent a significant amount of time researching window manufacturers. I paid for high-end wood/aluminum, low E-argon, double-pane windows with many extra features. However, when I was on site watching installation, the general tradesman looked at my windows and said, "Oh, no, not them." I was surprised to learn from an installation perspective why the windows were inferior to others. The contractor can be a wealth of information and assistance when selecting finishing materials. If you allow the contractor to purchase finishing materials, ensure that the price is competitive and the product is right for you. Within the contract, reserve the right to select your own suppliers for finishing *and,* if possible, for structural materials.

*If you allow the contractor to purchase finishing materials, ensure that the price is competitive and the product is right for you. Within the contract, reserve the right to select your own suppliers for finishing and, if possible, for structural materials.*

A sample finishing materials worksheet has been provided in appendix 3 for your referral. Since all renovation projects are unique, creating your own worksheet would be beneficial. Please visit the Renovation Management Company website at www.reno-management.com for a more detailed materials worksheet. You can consider copying this sheet and stapling it to the outside of a duo folder. Carry the folder with you to home shows and retail building supply stores. A record of your selections should be recorded on the worksheet, and any brochures and pictures can be stored in the folder. Once construction commences, give a copy of the worksheet to the contractor for reference.

## LABOR

With the cost of materials in hand, you will need to estimate the labor side of the equation. Table 7.4 shows average contractor labor costs to construct a 3,500-square-foot home. Estimates of hours and U.S. national average trade labor rates (including insurance and benefits) have been applied. With contractors' labor rates, you can calculate your contractors' labor costs that will initiate negotiations with your contractor. To further refine your labor estimate and confirm current labor rates within your local area, contact your local building center, homeowners' association and several estimator companies posted on the Internet. The Craftsman Book Company (www.craftsman-book.com) publishes for the construction industry, but homeowners can download the "National Estimator Service," which supplies labor rates and adjustment percentages by state and province. The download is quick; however, the information is extensive, so calling the help desk is an option. They can direct you to the labor rate information within minutes.

For rough calculations, review the following average trades with your contractor and ask approximately how many days each trade will take to complete their job.

**Table 7.4   Major Labor Costs for 3,500 Sq. Ft. Home**

| Trade | # of Tradespeople per day | × | Total hrs. (# of days × 8 hrs.) | × | Labor rate* per hr. | = Total Cost |
|---|---|---|---|---|---|---|
| General Tradespeople (framers or carpenters) | 4 | × | 480 (60 × 8) | × | $30 | = $57,600 |
| Electricians | 2 | × | 80 (10 × 8) | × | $35 | = 5,600 |
| Plumbers | 2 | × | 80 (10 × 8) | × | $35 | = 5,600 |
| Masons | 2 | × | 80 (10 × 8 | × | $28 | = 4,480 |
| Drywall (Sheetrock) installer | 2 | × | 120 (15 × 8) | × | $28 | = 6,720 |
| Painters | 2 | × | 80 (10 × 8) | × | $30 | = 4,800 |
| Bricklayers/ Stucco Applicators | 2 | × | 120 (15 × 8) | × | $30 | = 7,200 |
| Excavators | 2 | × | 24 (3 × 8) | × | $35 | = 1,680 |
| Roofers | 2 | × | 80 (10 × 8) | × | $32 | = 5,120 |
| Total average labor cost | | | | | | $98,800 |

*Labor rates are based on national U.S. averages. For average Canadian rates, apply current exchange rates.

The trades listed above make up most of your labor cost. The number of days for any remaining specialty trades required for your custom project that are not listed above should be estimated within your calculations. For example, if demolition work is required, you will need to budget hours for a demolition team.

# MISCELLANEOUS EXPENSES

Your contractor may already own most of the required equipment, such as bulldozers, scaffolding or dumpsters, and the cost of using the equipment may be covered within the 25% to 30% project management fee. On the other hand, your contractor may have to rent equipment and charge you an equipment rental fee. You will need to verify the equipment to be rented and call your local building supply store for a rental estimate.

Having completed the top 10 labor and materials costs, you can begin to apply your contractor's project management fee and markups to your calculations in order to complete a rough project estimate. As an example, table 7.5 illustrates a project estimate for the 3,500-square-foot home. The estimate includes a 30% contractor management fee applied to the retail price of the structural labor and materials costs before tax. A 10% materials markup was applied to only the structural materials before tax. Complete your own totals remembering to apply your local area tax rate and confirm and include any equipment rental charges.

**Table 7.5   Project Estimate for 3,500 Sq. Ft.**

| | | |
|---|---|---|
| Cost of top 10 structural materials before tax | $41,325 | |
| Add 30% contractor management fee | $12,398 | |
| Add 10% contractor materials markup | $ 4,133 | |
| Cost of top 10 finishing materials | $91,300 | |
| Total cost top 10 materials before tax | | $149,156 |
| Labor cost before tax | $98,800 | |
| Add 30% contractor management fee | 29,640 | |
| Total labor cost before tax | | $128,440 |
| Total project estimate based on top 10 materials, excluding tax | | $277,596 |

This chapter has provided you with the essential tools to prepare your own project estimate. Every renovation project seems to have unique designs that require problem solving and careful costing analysis. Armed with an understanding of construction, the top standard materials, contractors' expectations regarding profits and methods contractors use to prepare an estimate, you are better prepared to formulate your own estimate customized to your project. Once your estimate is complete, you are ready to meet with your contractor to review the estimate he or she has prepared.

The next chapter provides you with insight into how to best modify both your and your contractor's estimate in order to produce one final estimate.

# 8 Deciphering Your Contractor's Estimate

*"I hired a translator fluent in French, German, Japanese and Contractor."*

---

Having prepared your own project estimate, you will feel more confident working your way through the variety of formats contractors use when presenting their calculations. Important in your first contractor meeting is to confirm the format your contractor plans to submit. Ideally, to minimize the length of your estimate meeting, your contractor should detail labor, structural and finishing materials, project management fees and equipment rentals separately. In this way, your numbers can be easily compared with what your contractor presents.

If a contractor hesitates to provide full estimate disclosure, this may be an indication of poor concern with detail or of a number of potential hidden markups. Both situations are undesirable and start you off on the wrong foot. Your contractor may agree to provide as much detail as possible, yet when the time comes to review an estimate, the layout may not be what you expected.

At one extreme, your contractor may present you with just a total number. During your initial contractor meetings, explain to the contractor that the totals are not acceptable. However, if despite your preparations, you are faced with evaluating a total, prepare yourself for a lengthy meeting. Essentially, you will need to do the contractor's job of breaking down and reworking the numbers. Unless you firmly believe in the contractor or he or she recognizes the mistake and makes an honest effort the second time around, I would just walk away from this deal.

If your contractor's homework has been done, get ready to evaluate your numbers against what your contractor has prepared. One of the most popular contractor estimate formats is an itemized "to do" list with a combined labor and materials estimate beside each action item. (See figure 8.1.) In order to effectively evaluate your contractor's estimate against your calculations, you should discuss and break down his or her labor, structural and finishing materials totals and reformat your calculations to ensure you are comparing apples to apples. This is a give-and-take process as you work on adding and subtracting both your and your contractor's numbers.

Figure 8.1 illustrates a sample homeowner's notations penciled beside the contractor's estimate. The homeowner's notations have been derived from costs calculated in chapter 7, but have been reformatted—added together by task to allow for a comparison with the contractor's format.

---

FIGURE 8.1    **Sample Homeowner's Notations against Contractor's Estimate**

**ACME GENERAL CONTRACTOR—QUOTE FOR MR. SMITH'S 3,500 SQ. FT. RESIDENCE**

| TASK | QUOTE | HOMEOWNER'S NOTATIONS | |
|------|-------|----------------------|--|
| ▌Excavate and build foundation | $28,000 | *Labor* | *$6,100* |
| | | *Materials* | *$12,000* |
| | | *Markup* | *$5,000* |
| | | *Total* | *$23,100* |

| | | | |
|---|---|---|---|
| ▌ Construct frame (2 × 4 stud walls, roof, sheathing, garage) | $127,000 | *Labor* | *$46,000* |
| | | *Materials* | *$44,800* |
| | | *Markup* | *$25,000* |
| | | *Total* | *$115,800* |
| ▌ Insulate and drywall | $25,000 | *Labor* | *$10,200* |
| | | *Materials* | *$7,800* |
| | | *Markup* | *$5,000* |
| | | *Total* | *$23,000* |
| ▌ Installation of all electrical, plumbing, ductwork | $24,000 | *Labor* | *$13,200* |
| | | *Materials* | *$7,000* |
| | | *Markups* | *$4,700* |
| | | *Total* | *$24,900* |
| ▌ Complete all painting/exterior finishes | $34,800 | *Labor* | *$13,000* |
| | | *Materials* | *$9,000* |
| | | *Markups* | *$4,200* |
| | | *Total* | *$26,200* |
| ▌ Install interior including kitchen, bathroom, doors and closets | $90,000 | *Labor* | *$10,000* |
| | | *Materials* | *$52,000* |
| | | *Markup* | *$3,000* |
| | | *Total* | *$65,000* |
| Total labor and top 10 materials estimate (excluding tax) | $330,000 | *Total* | *$278,000* |

Remember the contractor's estimation for all of your finishing materials is a budget and guideline for you to follow as you select your materials from your local supplier. Make a decision about how much *you* would like to spend on finishing materials and stay focused on the amounts your contractor has budgeted for structural materials and labor.

Only by preparing your own estimate can you engage the contractor in a detailed discussion about why your calculations are so different. If you find you are confused by any of your contractor's explanations, ensure you ask for clarification. Both of you will probably recalculate numbers to arrive at a mutually agreed amount.

*Only by preparing your own estimate can you engage the contractor in a detailed discussion about why your calculations are so different.*

In figure 8.1, the contractor's numbers have been purposely overstated by a total of $52,000 to illustrate how contractor's estimates can differ from homeowners' calculations. Only upon careful analysis and discussions would the homeowner be able to determine that the contractor mistakenly applied a 10% markup to finishing materials. Further, the contractor's calculations include waste and the 20% remainder structural materials not accounted for in the homeowner's calculations.

Interestingly, once the remainder of the structural and finishing materials, waste, markup and tax are included in the homeowner's 3,500-square-foot home cost calculations, the cost per square foot starts to average a little over $100. Important to remember is that this per-square-foot amount includes *all* finishing materials. If your contractor quotes on a per-square-foot basis, you will need to carefully review what your contractor has included within this amount against your own calculations.

Comparing your calculations with your contractor's can be a rewarding and confidence-building process. You will feel as though you have a better understanding of your project and feel your participation has made a difference to its success. The review of variances between your numbers and the contractor's will prompt a discussion and allow you to identify those contractors who have lowballed, or those who have inflated an estimate. No longer do you have to rely on gut feelings based on a contractor's interpersonal skills. You are in the driver's seat and you will be able to decide whether you want to continue a relationship or hold out and wait for the next contractor to come along.

The next chapter reviews one of the most important elements to maintaining a successful relationship with your contractor—the contract. In many cases, contracts are considered a necessary, but sometimes not carefully crafted, document. Prior to construction, the completion of a well-prepared contract may not be of high priority; however, once construction commences, your contract becomes critical to your construction project. Of primary importance is that all agreements be signed *prior* to any work being done by the contractor on site. If work begins before a contract is signed, you have lost a significant negotiation advantage. Chapter 9 provides insight into the contract process and the essential elements to include in a contract that will help to keep your contractor working to schedule.

# 9 Negotiating, Signing and Maintaining the Contract:
## The Essentials in the Game of Survivor

*"That was all covered in the fine print."*

Once your project is underway, the level of detail in your contract is the single most important item that will help you to manage your project. All of the prework that has been described in the past eight chapters should be outlined in your contractual document. If you happen to leave an item off the contract, you are at the mercy of the contractor who may either stand by verbal agreements or bill over and above the contract. Below is a check-list for you to refer to when completing the contract:

✔ The contractor will build to the plan as attached.
✔ The contractor will install materials that are not shown in the attached plan but indicated below.
✔ The contractor will obtain all building permits that are not completed by the architect.
✔ The contractor will build to code and rework, at his or her expense, any area requiring correction to pass inspection.
✔ The contractor will hire only certified tradespeole.
✔ Required subcontractors are identified and all subcontractors are licensed. Reserve the right to hire your own subcontractors.

✔ Release of liens signed by subcontractors and contractor protecting the homeowner from liens against his or her property from the subcontractors or suppliers looking for payments.

✔ The contractor has on-site insurance and workers' compensation/disability.

✔ Payment schedule (discussed in more detail in this chapter).

✔ All contractor's fees and contractor markups on materials and labor are listed and all-inclusive.

✔ Materials that the homeowner is responsible for purchasing and the materials that the contractor is responsible for.

✔ The contractor agrees to a minimum one-year work warranty and agrees to turn over to the homeowner all manufacturer warranties and instruction manuals.

✔ Agreement to meet every two weeks to review schedules and labor/materials versus budget. Agreement for the contractor to supply all invoices upon request.

✔ Document of change control. If changes are made to the original plans during construction, include an agreement about how the contractor will reestimate, seek approval and revise timelines.

Contract details are essential and will help to avoid costly and time-consuming court battles during construction. Both homeowners and contractors want to avoid putting their lives on hold to sit in a court room. If a contract is buttoned down with black-and-white detail, both parties will be able to weigh the probability of success within court and, it is hoped, resolve issues prior to contacting a lawyer. Without a solid contract, you will have the unpopular decision about whether or not to continue with the project or to stop construction for mediation, arbitration or litigation.

In some instances, you may have an opportunity to hire a contractor friend or relative to work on your construction project. An official document with someone close to you may seem unnecessary, and some feel uncomfortable discussing the subject. However, what happens if your friend is called away on an emergency and a short-term replacement is sent? Or, since you are good friends, perhaps you wouldn't mind if your friend put you on hold for just a little while for a great, profitable contracting opportunity. Many different situations can arise that can test your patience with relatives or friends, particularly when it involves a significant amount of your money. A well-detailed contract is important to maintaining friendships and relationships with your relatives.

*A well-detailed contract is important to maintaining friendships and relationships with your relatives.*

I've interviewed people in both successful working relationships and unsuccessful ones. Having a contract completed ahead of time is not an indication that you don't trust your relatives. Rather, a contract is a document that provides clarification and clears up any misunderstandings if either party was away from the site for a period of time.

Remember that reputable contractors who have been in the business for some time are completely aware of the importance of solid contracts. Completing a detailed contract is all in the course of a day's business. Those contractors who shy away from details are sending a signal that perhaps they are not for you. Honesty, honesty, honesty is the motto. Without basic trust, your project will deteriorate to on-the-spot haggling and exasperation. The more agreed to in writing, the fewer variables and the less frustration. If contractor relationships deteriorate too far, you may be faced with putting a halt to the construction and changing contractors midstream.

Many of us have seen projects in our neighborhood at a standstill. The first thought is that the poor homeowner didn't manage his or her finances and may be forced to sell. The next time you drive by a vacant job site, consider that homeowners will rarely embark upon a project knowing that the cost will put them into financial ruin. Instead, the homeowners may have employed a disreputable contractor, and the project may have run too far over the initial estimate. Further, the homeowners may have failed to effectively analyze the quote, sign a detailed contract and manage the project. Frustrated and in disbelief, the homeowners may have refused to pay invoices until matters were resolved. Unfortunately, the contractor may pull the workers and move onto another profitable project. Without a detailed contract, the process of resolving the dispute could take forever. The homeowner may be faced with finding another contractor to finish the job.

Changing contractors midstream can be a tricky and expensive business. First, some contractors may be reluctant to take over where one has left off because of construction warranties. For example, what happens if the basement leaks or an installed window cracks? The question becomes, which contractor comes back to fix the problem at no cost? Or, perhaps the first contractor didn't abide by building or electrical codes. The first contractor should fix the problem free of charge, but now you have a second contractor involved who should charge for the service.

To complicate matters further, one of the reasons for firing your first contractor may be due to skyrocketing costs over and above the original quote. You will be looking for a good deal from the second contractor who may be too busy with more profitable jobs to bother.

Selecting the right contractor and preparing a solid contract is critical for the success of your job. A personable contractor, friend or relative is always helpful since, in some cases, you'll be spending more time with this person during the project than with your partner. However, you are in business together, with a significant amount of money involved. No matter what the circumstance, a well-researched, detailed contract that is satisfying to both you and your contractor helps to anchor the project, minimize misunderstandings and keep contractor relationships professional.

## NEGOTIATION

Negotiation is a funny thing. Those who have dealt with a good negotiator are not even aware that they have been manipulated. The negotiator is so outstanding in subtlety that others become convinced and committed to wonderful ideas they believe were their own.

Negotiation is an art to be mastered. Those who need to work on their skills are those who leave others with feelings of resentment and frustration that the negotiator doesn't understand their needs. Nobody likes to know that they have been suckered into a deal. In fact, those who feel suckered usually put their foot down and won't budge on a point because of the principle of it. If you are the negotiator and this happens to you, then you need to brush up on your skills. To manipulate others into a solution that satisfies and motivates *all* parties involved requires talent.

Below are tips to help you in negotiations with your contractor:

## UNDERSTAND YOUR CONTRACTOR'S NEEDS AND MOTIVATIONS

Listen to your contractor and try to determine how you can benefit from your contractor's situation while still meeting your needs. For example, ask if your contractor is predicting business to slow over the next year. Perhaps you can adjust your start schedule to a slower time and negotiate a better price. Understanding your contractor's needs may open up barter opportunities. For example, your contractor may need a new truck and you may have connections in the trucking business. Listening and getting to know your contractor will help you negotiate a few items that could be of benefit to both of you.

## GATHER INFORMATION AND KNOW YOUR PROJECT

First and foremost, the information provided in this book puts you in a truly advantageous position and provides you with negotiating power. A contractor may rely on your inexperience to gain agreements in their favor. Those who have an understanding of the industry will be more effective in negotiating solutions before, during and after construction.

Keep in mind that all construction projects have unique problems to be solved. As such, you need to gather information and to understand as much as possible about your construction project. Stop anybody who starts to talk beyond your understanding and ask for clarification.

As soon as you have no idea what the contractor is talking about, you lose the ability to constructively negotiate. For example, if you don't know what a certain material is for, how can you determine how much you will need and how long it will take to install?

Further, titles such as "plumber" and "electrician" bring creditability. A plumber, for example, may tell you a long story about why you should upgrade and replace something; it sounds impressive, but you have difficulty understanding the solution as presented. Evaluating what is proposed becomes difficult (if not impossible) and what may have sounded impressive may not be the best solution to solving your problem. For example, I was told that an old iron pipe needed to be completely replaced since drilling would cause the pipe to shatter. Maybe true, maybe not. I phoned around and determined that, as long as the plumber is careful, the pipe will probably be fine. I decided to hire a plumber that drilled and saved myself $1,000.

We can place a great deal of trust in what is said by those who have a title. If you are listening to a tradesperson giving you an explanation for what is required to be done, and a little voice is whispering, "You've got to be kidding," then I would advise you to get another opinion. Another opinion would provide you with the information needed to effectively negotiate options with your contractor.

Remember to slow down conversations and ensure you understand the nuts and bolts of what is being discussed.

## WIN-WIN ATTITUDE

Important for the homeowner to remember is that contractors are in the business to make money. All businesses need to be profitable; otherwise, the company will not succeed. When negotiating with your contractor, both parties need to be satisfied with the agreement. If one party starts to take advantage of a situation, the relationship begins to deteriorate and the project can fall apart. Negotiation is not about gaining reluctant agreement from the other party. Rather, when negotiating, the other party needs to be nodding in agreement with the thought that this deal is right for him or her. The meeting should conclude with the contractor feeling satisfied and enthusiastic about your upcoming project. You should feel a sense of accomplishment in your negotiations when your needs have been met and you have achieved your goals with a contractor who walks away satisfied. Both parties are committed and ready to begin.

## TIME SPENT = QUALITY NEGOTIATIONS

Have you ever been in a situation where you rushed into a retail store expecting a quick deal and found none were to be had? On the flip side, have you ever been in a situation where you walked into a retail store, taken an enormous amount of the sales rep's time and eventually found the savings materializing? The difference between the two situations is that the sales rep becomes more and more committed to the sales situation and enters into "the zone." The zone is that magical time when the "I can let you have it for …" is said. The sales rep has invested time in a sales situation and doesn't want to find out that you are going to walk out without purchasing anything. The rep doesn't want to feel that time has been wasted with a customer. The zone is the time that the sales person is ready to close the sale and ask for your money.

With respect to your dealings with contractors, the greater the amount of time they have invested with you in discussing and pricing your project, the easier the transition to the zone and the more constructive your negotiations will be.

## GOOD COP, BAD COP

Many of you are familiar with this tactic. In order to move negotiations along, one person plays the tough guy while the other plays the nice guy. The nice guy is the mediator between the tough guy and the contractor. To be successful, you will need to strategize with your partner prior to meeting with the contractor to determine who is bad and who is good. You will agree on the goals for the meeting and agree to remain flexible, depending on how the situation goes. The tough guy should try to stick to the bad guy role while the good guy positions himself or herself on the contractor's side. The good guy approaches the contractor in a "let's see what just you and I can work out together" attitude. This strategy helps to open up negotiations and concessions between the contractor and the good guy.

The good cop, bad cop strategy has been used for years. Many, including police officers, who coined the phrase, use this approach. In fact, if you were to think about it, you have probably applied the approach without even realizing it. For some, the good cop, bad cop strategy comes about naturally. One partner is usually a little more hardnosed than the other. Either way, now that you are more aware of how the process works, you can have a little fun applying it.

## COMPETITION ALWAYS HELPS

Let your contractor know that others are bidding on the project. A little competition can encourage more aggressive pricing. In some cases, if you are finding that a contractor is reluctant to make concessions in certain areas, you can use the others to your advantage. Ensure that the reluctant contractor is aware that the other contractors are willing to comply. Remember you have the power, the money and the possibility of becoming a future client reference. Contractors are keen to win your business. In fear of losing the project, the reluctant contractor may change his or her mind. However, as mentioned earlier, use your own cost estimate in negotiations to ensure the contractor has not lowballed the estimate.

## THE COLUMBO

Do you remember Peter Falk in the TV show *Columbo*? His claim to fame in solving mysteries was to leave his most significant question to the very end of the conversation. After a lengthy and exhaustive friendly interrogation, Columbo would begin to exit from the scene only to pause and say, "Only one more little thing to ask." This "little thing" was typically the most important question to solving the crime, and the response was usually what Columbo wanted to hear.

The message here is the timing of your negotiations. If you have a priority item to negotiate, you may want to consider slipping it into the end of your conversation. In some cases, the contractor could already have his or her shoes on and be heading out the door and you could say, "Oh, yeah, the labor rate, if I were to agree to a variable labor charge could you bring the general tradesmen's labor rate down to $25 per hour?" Timing and casual phrasing are the critical elements. You may find that the contractor is so tired and ready to end the conversation that you receive a positive response.

## TIME TO THINK

Occasionally, you may find a contractor rushing you to make a decision. Under pressure, you may agree to what is being said, only to think about it later in bed and realize you made a mistake. Whether intentionally or not, contractors can be working on many projects at one time and try to rush you to a decision. I have had situations where a contractor expected an immediate check after handing me an invoice while standing on a boat in the pouring rain. Unfortunately, due to the pressure, I paid, only to look at the invoice later on and realize it was all wrong. Remember to maintain control by taking your time on decisions that you feel require more thought.

## KEEP EMOTIONS AT BAY

In order to think and negotiate clearly, we need to take a deep breath and keep our emotions in check. Knowing how the system works will be a confidence booster, but remember to check your ego at the door. Once you have lost your temper, you've typically lost the argument and may damage the underlying relationship. Many contractors put in an honest day's work and you don't want to frighten away the good ones.

## KEEPING YOUR CONTRACTOR ON THE JOB

Having done all your homework, you will be able to negotiate a fair deal for both you and your contractor. However, during boom times when labor supply is low and demand is high, a contractor and the tradespeople will gravitate toward the more profitable jobs. You may experience long delays and find yourself wondering when a crew will show up. A project schedule should be included within your contract; however, unforeseen delays can put your project on the back burner. The solution to keeping your contractor on the job is money, money and money.

Although the past eight chapters have talked about ways to save money, this chapter talks about spending money. The difference lies in the control you have over the billing process and the honest, up-front contractual arrangements that keep both you and your contractor happy. You don't have to worry about sneaky hidden charges and the contractor doesn't have to worry about doing it. Both of you have agreed upon a win-win formula that offers financial incentives to help keep your project moving.

First and foremost, a payment schedule should be included in your contract. A payment schedule includes a contractor's project schedule with specific payment amounts. The project schedule will indicate what is to be completed and when, and the payment schedule outlines how much is to be paid. Many times, payments are based on the percentage of your total project cost with little thought to actual costs incurred to date. Now that you have a better understanding of your project costs, you have the ability to approximate your contractor's actual expenses as the project progresses. To determine your payment schedule, refer back to your estimate and calculate your contractor's labor and materials expenses (including project management fees, materials markups and tax) incurred upon completion of specific tasks.

For example, your first payment may be made upon completion of the foundation and basement ceiling. Add up all the materials, labor, contractor fees and tax to arrive at your first payment amount. Stay alert to those contractors who demand a significant amount of money up front prior to the commencement of your project. Most reputable contractors have 30-day terms with their materials suppliers and labor usually paid at the end of a construction month. Avoid deposits and write your first check as outlined in your payment schedule. If your contractor expresses concern over receiving payment for work performed, inform your contractor that a signed contract is a legal document between both parties and should serve as sufficient reassurance that payments will be made. Depending on the size of your project and construction timelines, your first payment is typically made at the end of the first construction month.

*Depending on the size of your project and construction timelines, your first payment is typically made at the end of the first construction month.*

Most contractors are motivated to finish a project since money isn't made when a project sits idle. A contractor would like to finish as soon as possible to get paid. However, in boom times many contractors are busy 24/7 and will prioritize the more profitable jobs. If you are concerned that your contractor and the team may be unable to stick to your project schedule, consider assigning specific dates with bonus payments in the contract.

The amount paid in bonus depends on how busy the contractor is, how much the contractor has asked for and how much of a priority it is for you to complete the project on time. As an example, a generous bonus is to double the 10% contractor profit (contained within the 25% to 30% project management fee) for completing on schedule. Adding an extra 10% for completing on time is a substantial incentive. However, if the project is delayed beyond a contractual date, the incentive drops to 8% and then to 5%, and so on. Finally, if the date exceeds the 0% mark you can consider penalties.

As a smaller incentive, some homeowners have offered an additional 10% to the project management fee total dollars. For example, if your contractor has estimated receiving $30,000 in management fees, an extra 10% to complete on time would award your contractor an extra

$3,000 ($30,000 × 10%). The amount of incentive is flexible, but the higher the incentive the greater the probability of the contractor meeting the schedule.

A penalty is difficult to discuss with the contractor since penalties cast a negative tone to the contract. Many people attach a penalty to a date set very far out—a date that the contractor claims, "No way will the project be done by that date." As you discuss penalties, remind your contractor that you both have an agreement to handle changes during construction.

As previously mentioned, your contract should include details on how changes are to be managed once the project is underway—commonly referred to as a change control process. Inevitably, changes to plans are made on site as a result of construction obstacles or home-owner revisions. Once the change has been identified, your contractor should respond within a determined timeline with a revised estimate, project schedule and timeline. Upon your approval of the revisions, all incentives and penalties will need to be adjusted to reflect the revised date. As long as your contractor knows that allowances for changes have been included in the contract, discussing penalties should not be difficult.

The amount of the penalty should be the cost of inconvenience. If you were required to vacate your home and rent accommodation, the penalty should equate to the amount spent on alternative housing. Or, if you were living in the home, but unable to live in half the building, consider half the cost of your monthly mortgage as a starting point. However determined, the penalty is subtracted from the total cost of the project. Penalties should be documented within the contract.

The final contractor invoice that adds or subtracts bonus or penalty payments should not be paid for at least eight weeks following the completion of your construction project. The delay helps to ensure that all suppliers and employees have been paid by your contractor and won't come looking to you for payment.

The past nine chapters have been devoted to providing you with insight into the construction industry, home building, estimates and contracts. Proper understanding of all of these elements is critical to effective contractor management. Those homeowners who charge into a construction project without an understanding of what is ahead of them, open the door to disaster. Those who have blindly hired an honest contractor may be lucky. Yet a staggering number of North American homeowners lodge complaints every year concerning contractors who overcharge, deliver poor quality and are behind schedule. Preparation and education are your best defense against becoming a dissatisfied statistic.

It is my hope that this book will help you to select contractors who deserve our business and our support.

# 10 Only the Honest Will Survive

The Wise Renovator

As with every economic cycle, what goes up must come down. Baby boomers, those born between 1945 and 1965, have been a major force in industrial economic swings. The combination of baby boomers' purchasing power and the fluctuations of interest rates have significantly affected the housing market and the construction industry.

In the 1970s, boomers turned 20 and entered the housing market. Housing prices started to climb and inflation took off as boomers bought furniture, appliances and every item to fill their new home. Climbing interest rates took a bite out of the 1970's market until the 1980s when boomers had a little more money and looked to upgrade to monster-sized homes. In the 1990s, boomers were settled with children and have been renovating ever since. Low interest rates have further supported a housing and renovation boom in the 2000s. The echo generation (boomers' children) is now entering the first-time home buyer's market, and boomers continue to renovate. All of these factors translate to a hot construction industry. The question remains, how long the industry will continue to thrive.

Some believe interest rates will remain low for many years ahead since boomers are approaching retirement and focusing their energies on saving. Many feel that boomers have purchased all the furniture and appliances needed for retirement and that the spending power of the echo generation is not strong enough to stimulate the economy and drive up the inflation rates that we experienced back in the 1970s and 1980s.

Further, boomers who are sitting on million-dollar 4,000-square-foot homes and have lost their retirement savings in the stock market will look to their personal residences for retirement cash. Within the next 10 to 15 years, a mass of monster-sized homes are predicted to flood the market, while demand for smaller high-end bungalow style homes will exceed supply. This prediction is further supported by the fact that rarely do you find people in their 80s living alone in a 4,000-square-foot home. Definitely it's a buyer's delight for the echo generation looking to trade up and sell their smaller starter home.

Others feel interest rate increases are inevitable and the construction industry has had its heyday. History has confirmed many times over that the housing market experiences highs and lows. It remains to be seen when the next dip will occur.

As witnessed in the past, as soon as the construction industry starts to slow, contractors and tradespeople find work hard to come by and have to be more price and service competitive. Contractors who have failed to develop solid reputations during prosperous times will have difficulty winning contracts during slower times.

Whether the construction industry is accelerating or decelerating, effective contractor management will help to pave the way to a successful projcct.

# Appendix 1
## R-Value Insulation and
## Square-Foot Coverage

| R-VALUE | COVERAGE IN SQUARE FEET |
|---------|-------------------------|
| R-5 | 16 |
| R-12 | 88 |
| R-13 | 58 |
| R-14 | 59 |
| R-20 | 49 |
| R-22 | 34 |
| R-28 | 43 |
| R-31 | 43 |
| R-35 | 38 |
| R-40 | 27 |

# Appendix 2
## Formulas for Remaining Structural Materials

This section is a continuation of chapter 7. Chapter 7 provided the top 10 most expensive structural materials of a 3,500-square-foot home. Below are all the remaining structural materials calculated with average U.S. retail pricing.

### 2 × 2 CROSSBAR BRIDGES

The 2 × 2 crossbar bridges sit between the joists, side by side every 6 lineal feet along the short side or width of the floor. The width of the basement ceiling is 31 feet. Five sets of crossbars would run the width of the room (31 ft. ÷ 6). To run the 59-foot length, 59 rows are required. Approximately 2 feet of a 2 × 2 board is required per crossbar and 3 floors will be supported. Each board is 8 feet long; divide the total by 8 to determine the number of 2 × 2 boards needed. The formula:

$$\frac{[(\underline{\text{Floor Width} \times \text{Floor Length}}) \times 2/8] \times 3}{6}$$

#### ■ NUMBER OF 2 × 2 BOARDS

Basement ceiling (31 ft. ÷ 6) × 59 = 304 × 2/8 × 3 floors       180
   Average cost per board ($1.90 × 180)                       $342

### 2 × 12 STAIR STRINGERS

One 20-foot 2 × 12 is used on either side of the stair runway. Measure the length of the stair diagonal. Determine how many 20-foot 2 × 12s are required by dividing the length by 20. Don't forget to double the number to include stringers on both sides of all stairways.

■ **NUMBER OF 20 FT. 2 × 12s**

Stringer 20 ft. 2 × 12 boards                                          4

   Average cost per board ($26.60 × 4)                                          $106

## 2 × 10 SILL PLATES

A sill plate is a 2 × 10 board that is anchored to the footings and runs around the entire perimeter. The ends of the floor joists rest on top of the sill plate. To calculate out the number of boards required, measure the entire length of your footings and divide by 20-foot boards.

■ **NUMBER OF 20 FT. 2 × 10s**

180 ÷ 20 ft. boards                                          9

   Average cost per board ($20.40 × 9)                                          $184

## DRYCORE

Optional product used directly on top of the concrete to finish basement floors (see chapter 5). Each sheet covers 4 square feet. To calculate the number of boards, divide the basement square footage by 4.

■ **NUMBER OF 2 × 2 FT. DRYCORE SHEETS**

800 sq. ft. ÷ 4                                          200

   Average cost per sheet ($5.40 × 200)                                          $1,075

## ASPHALT

Asphalt sits on top of the driveway gravel and is purchased by the ton. To calculate tonnage, multiply the required cubic feet by 148 (pounds of asphalt required per cubic foot). To determine tonnage, divide by 2000 (2000 pounds = one ton). **Note:** Due to oil price fluctuations, hot-mix asphalt price per ton varies *widely* between state and province. Check local rates for your calculations. A 4-inch base has been applied in the calculations below. Depth varies by state and province.

■ **NUMBER OF TONS**

| | | |
|---|---|---|
| 267 cu. ft. × 148 ÷ 2000 | 20 | |
| Average cost per ton ($50 × 20) | | $1,000 |

## PLASTIC SHEATHING/VAPOR BARRIER

Referred to as Polyethylene. Calculate the total square footage or refer to previous calculations for the following areas as required:

1. Basement floor—under concrete and above concrete
2. Exterior walls—including basement
3. Underneath hardwood (optional)
4. Interior of the roof

Polyethylene is sold in 1,500-square-foot rolls, divide the total by 1,500 to determine the number of rolls required.

■ **NUMBER OF POLYETHYLENE ROLLS**

| | | | |
|---|---|---|---|
| Basement floor | 1,829 sq.ft. | | |
| Exterior wall | 4,320 sq. ft. | | |
| Hardwood floors | 2,531 sq. ft. | | |
| Interior roof | 2,160 sq. ft. | | |
| TOTAL | 10,840 sq. ft. ÷ 1,500 sq. ft. roll | 8 | |
| Average cost per roll ($43.10 × 8) | | | $345 |

## WIRE MESH

Used to reinforce the basement and garage concrete floor, wire mesh is purchased in 4 × 8 (32-square-foot) sections. Divide the basement square footage by 32 to determine the number of sections.

■ **NUMBER OF 4 × 8 SECTIONS**

| | | | |
|---|---|---|---|
| Basement | 1,829 sq. ft. | | |
| Garage floor | 400 sq. ft. | | |
| TOTAL | 2,229 sq. ft. ÷ 32 | 70 | |
| Average cost per section ($6.00 × 70) | | | $420 |

# REBAR

Rebar is inserted into the ready-mix (concrete) footings and concrete wall for reinforcement. Half-inch bars can be purchased up to 8 feet long. For footings, two bars run horizontally along side the perimeter length of the footing. Measure the total footings perimeter for both the basement and garage. Divide by 8 and multiply by 2. If you are building a concrete wall as opposed to a block wall, rebar will be inserted vertically every 2 feet up to the top of the concrete form. An 8-foot bar will be roughly sufficient to meet the top of the form. Apply the same lineal total as above and divide by 2 to calculate the number of rebars for the foundation wall.

■ **NUMBER OF 8-FOOT REBARS**

| | | |
|---|---|---|
| Footings house 180 ft. ÷ (8 × 2) | 45 | |
| Footings garage 80 ft. ÷ (8 × 2) | 20 | |
| Basement walls 180 ft ÷ 2 | 90 | |
| Total number of rods | 155 | |
| Average cost per bar ($3 × 155) | | $465 |

# MORTAR

Mortar is used between cinder blocks and for two coats of wall parge. The contractor will mix cement with sand and water to create the correct consistency. On average, one bag of cement will lay 28 cinder blocks. Divide the total number of cinder blocks by 28 to determine the number of bags. Depending on the mortar manufacturer, one bag of sand is required per bag of cement.

The cinder blocks are sealed with parge mix. One 66-pound bag covers 42 square feet—one layer at 1/4-inch thick. Calculate your total square footage and divide by 42. Since two layers are recommended multiply by 2.

■ **NUMBER OF CEMENT BAGS**

675 cinder blocks ÷ 28                                              25

  Average cost per bag ($3.90 × 56)                                              $98

■ **NUMBER OF BAGS OF SAND**

Number of cement bags                                              56

  Average cost per bag ($4 × 56)                                              $224

■ **NUMBER OF BAGS OF PARGE MIX**

Garage wall 600 sq. ft. ÷ (42 × 2)                                              29

  Average cost per bag ($7.20 × 29)                                              $208

## JACK POSTS

Your architect or contractor will advise you about how many steel posts are required in the basement to support the first floor. Note the height and the number required.

## INTERIOR DRAINAGE

A floor drain inside the basement under the concrete is made of 3-inch PVC piping. Determine where the drain will be located on the floor and measure the distance to the where the sump pump is planned to determine how many feet of piping are required.

■ **NUMBER OF FEET OF 3-INCH PVC PIPE**

Basement floor drain                                              12

  Average cost per foot ($1.30 × 12)                                              $16

# EXTERIOR DRAINAGE

Weeping tile is purchased by the foot. Measure the footing's perimeter to determine the number of feet of weeping tile required. A 1-inch PVC drain pipe is imbedded in gravel by the window well and connects down to the perimeter drain/weeping tile. Since 10-foot pipes will be purchased and cut, multiply the number of wells by 10.

## ■ WEEPING TILE

| | | |
|---|---|---|
| Perimeter of house (feet) | 180 | |
|     Average cost per foot ($0.30 × 180) | | $54 |

## ■ 1-INCH DRAIN PIPE

| | | |
|---|---|---|
| 10 ft. × 3 | 30 | |
|     Average cost per foot ($0.40 × 30) | | $12 |

# ASPHALT COATING

Applied on top of the basement exterior wall. One pail covers 378 square feet. Divide the total square footage of basement walls by 378 to determine the number of pails. Since two coats are typically applied, multiply by 2.

## ■ NUMBER OF PAILS

| | | |
|---|---|---|
| Basement wall to ground level sq. ft. (1,440 ÷ 378) | 4 | |
|     Average cost per pail ($16 × 4) | | $64 |

# PLATON MEMBRANE

Optional layer on top of asphalt coating to improve moisture resistance. Platon is purchased in 394-foot rolls. Apply the basement wall square footage from above and divide by 394.

## ■ NUMBER OF ROLLS

| | | |
|---|---|---|
| Basement wall to ground level sq. ft. (1,440 ÷ 394) | 4 | |
|     Average cost per roll ($100 × 4) | | $400 |

## DRYWALL TAPE

Purchased in 500-foot rolls. Budget 12 feet of tape for every sheet of drywall. Multiply the number of sheet by 12 and divide by 500 to calculate the number of rolls.

### ■ NUMBER OF ROLLS

| | |
|---|---|
| Number of drywall sheets (327 × 12 ÷ 500) | 79 |
| Average cost per roll ($10 × 79) | $790 |

## MUD/DRYWALL COMPOUND

Four drywall sheets for every gallon of mud. Divide the number of drywall sheets by 4.

### ■ NUMBER OF GALLONS

| | |
|---|---|
| Number of drywall sheets (327 ÷ 4) | 82 |
| Average cost per gallon ($3 × 82) | $246 |

## METAL CORNER STRIPS

Count all the corners where one drywall sheet meets another to determine the number of strips to be purchased.

### ■ NUMBER OF 8-FOOT STRIPS

| | |
|---|---|
| Number of strips | 115 |
| Average cost per strip ($1.70 × 115) | $196 |

# DRYWALL SCREWS

Drywall screws are a very small budget item; however, have the formula handy: 24 screws per drywall sheet. Multiply the number of sheets by 24 and divide by 1,000 per box to determine the number of boxes.

### ■ NUMBER OF BOXES OF DRYWALL SCREWS

| | | |
|---|---|---|
| Number of drywall sheets (327 × 24 ÷ 1,000) | 8 | |
| Average cost per box ($13 × 8) | | $104 |

# CEMENT BOARDS/BACKER BOARDS

Installed on top of plywood subfloor prior to laying tile/stone, cement boards are purchased in 32-square-foot sheets. Calculate the total square footage and divide by 32.

### ■ NUMBER OF CEMENT BOARDS

| | | | |
|---|---|---|---|
| Kitchen | 239 sq. ft. | | |
| Bathroom | 434 sq. ft. | | |
| Front entrance | 18 sq. ft. | | |
| Fireplace floor mat(s) | 18 sq. ft. | | |
| Total sq. ft.  709 ÷ 32 | | 22 | |
| Average cost per sheet ($30 × 22) | | | $660 |

# FIREBOARD

Fireboard is attached to the fireplace stud frame. One board covers 32 square feet. Measure the square footage of your fireplace and divide by 32 square feet.

### ■ NUMBER OF BOARDS

| | | |
|---|---|---|
| Fireplaces frame(s) (160 sq. ft. ÷ 32) | 5 | |
| Average cost per board ($13 × 5) | | $85 |

## HOUSE WRAP/TYPAR

House Wrap is installed on top of the plywood sheathing on the outside of your house (above ground, not on foundation walls). This product is more popular as a final layer before brick—or final surface—versus rigid polystyrene as discussed under insulation. Measure the wall square footage around the house from ground to just below the roof. Typar comes in 900-square-foot rolls. Divide total square footage by 900.

### ■ NUMBER OF ROLLS

| | | |
|---|---|---|
| Exterior wall (3,133 sq. ft. ÷ 900) | 4 | |
| Average cost per roll ($80 × 4) | | $320 |

## WINDOW FLASHING, CAULKING, RED TAPE, INSULATION

Windows are usually waterproofed with flashing, a bead of caulking and red tape. Measure the perimeter of all windows and exterior glass doors. Flashing can be purchased in a variety of lengths; cost per lineal foot is illustrated below.

### ■ NUMBER OF FLASHING FEET

| | | |
|---|---|---|
| Windows and doors (308 lineal ft.) | 308 | |
| Average cost per foot ($2 × 308) | | $616 |

### ■ NUMBER OF CAULKING TUBES

| | | |
|---|---|---|
| Standard sized caulking tubes cover 50 lineal ft. standard bead size | | |
| 308 lineal ft. ÷ 50 lineal ft. coverage | 7 | |
| Average cost per tube ($4 × 7) | | $28 |

### ■ NUMBER OF ROLLS OF TAPE

| | | |
|---|---|---|
| Standard sized rolls cover approximately 164 lineal ft. | | |
| 308 ÷ 164 ft. of coverage | 2 | |
| Average cost per roll ($8 × 2) | | $16 |

## ■ NUMBER OF TUBES OF INSULATION

308 lineal ft. ÷ 250 lineal ft. per tube                                2

    Average cost per tube ($7 × 2)                                    $14

# ROOF FELT

Roof felt is laid on top of 1/2-inch plywood sheathing prior to the installation of shingles. Apply the square foot measurement from your plywood sheathing calculations. Roof felt is purchased in 430-square-foot rolls. Divide the total square footage by 430.

## ■ NUMBER OF ROLLS

3,328 sq. ft. ÷ 430                                                      8

    Average cost per roll ($17 × 8)                                   $136

# VALLEY FLASHING

Valley flashing is used to protect against moisture. Measure the number of feet where the roof meets a wall or another roof section. Usually sold in 8-inch wide strips.

## ■ NUMBER OF FEET

Number of ft. where roof meets the wall                                 150

    Average cost per ft. ($2 × 150)                                   $300

# RIDGE VENT

The ridge vent runs along the ridge board and is purchased in 20-foot rolls. Measure the length of the ridge board (refer to your previous lumber calculations). Divide the length by 20 to calculate the number of rolls needed.

## ■ NUMBER OF ROLLS

69 lineal ft. ÷ 20                                                       4

    Average cost per roll ($55 × 4)                                   $220

# DRIP EDGE

The drip edge attaches to the perimeter of the roof and is purchased by the foot. The length of drip edge required is the sum total of the roof perimeter.

## ■ NUMBER OF DRIP EDGE STRIPS

| | |
|---|---|
| Perimeter lineal ft. | 286 |
| Average cost per foot ($0.30 × 29) | $86 |

# DUCTS

For small renovations, your duct costs will be small. For new home construction, a rough calculation can be done to determine your approximate needs. The major materials include:

1. 5 ft. "L" main ducts
2. 5 ft. round pipes
3. Angle boots
4. Stack elbows
5. Floor and wall registers

Main ducts are rectangular shaped and are installed along the basement ceiling for air intake and outtake. Round pipe runs between the drywall to move air into rooms above the basement. The rest of the materials such as elbows, tees and fish collars are attached to round pipes and help direct air flow.

Main ducts are purchased in 5-foot-long "L" sections that are fastened together to create a rectangle. Measure the distance from the furnace to the farthest point away from the furnace. Since each "L" is 5 feet long, divide the number by 5; however, four "Ls" are required (two for the intake and two for the outtake). Multiply by 4 to calculate a total.

Round pipe connects to the main duct and runs up inside the walls throughout various rooms in your house. Plan on a minimum of one vent under every window in every room. Round pipe for the first floor will be connected to the main duct and run out to every window on the first floor. An angle boot connects to a round pipe and directs the air upwards to the first floor vent. Plan on one angle boot per first-floor vent.

Measure the length of your house to calculate the feet of round pipe needed to run from the main duct to the windows. Multiply the length by the number of first-floor windows. Since round pipe comes in 5-foot sections, divide by 5. Add an angle boot for every 5-foot round pipe. Added to the round pipe number are your upstairs needs and intake requirements. Measure the distance from the first floor to the floor of the top storey. Multiply by the number of vents on the top floor. Divide the number of feet by 5 to calculate how many 5-foot round pipe sections are required for the remaining floors. Add an angle boot for each pipe. To determine the amount of round pipe required for the air intake, ask your architect or contractor how many air intakes are required for your furnace and calculate the height distance for each intake to the furnace. Divide by 5 and add a stack elbow (used for wall registers) for each planned intake.

Add the number of floor and wall registers required. Additional materials, such as duct straps are required; however, the cost is insignificant.

## ■ NUMBER OF 5-FOOT MAIN DUCT SECTIONS

| | | |
|---|---|---|
| Basement (59 ft. ÷ 5 ft. sections × 4) | 48 | |
| Average cost per duct ($5 × 48) | | $240 |

## ■ NUMBER OF 5-FOOT ROUND PIPE SECTIONS

| | | |
|---|---|---|
| Width (main duct to first floor windows) 16 × 6 (number of windows) | 128 | |
| Height to top floor 8 × 8 | 64 | |
| Air intake (2 on main and 2 top floor) distance to furnace | 144 | |
| Oven duct to roof | 12 | |
| Total | 348 ÷ 5 = 70 | |
| Average cost per pipe ($4 × 70) | | $280 |

### ■ NUMBER OF ANGLE BOOTS
Total                                                        14
    Average cost per boot ($2.50 × 14)                                $35

### ■ NUMBER OF STACK ELBOWS
Total                                                        4
    Average cost per stack ($6 × 4)                                  $24

### ■ REGISTERS
Registers                                                    18
    Average cost per register ($8 × 18)                              $144

## PLUMBING

Major structural plumbing materials include a hot water tank, a meter, hot and cold water copper supply lines to run water throughout your house and ABS/PVC drain lines to drain water away. Refer to your architectural plans or local building codes for pipe sizes and materials. Without plans, rough formulas have been presented below.

For copper supply lines (example: 3/4-inch copper pipe), measure the distance in feet from the hot water tank to the opposite end of the basement. The first-floor faucets connect to the 3/4-inch basement copper lines. Add 4 feet for every faucet on the first floor to cover the distance from the basement lines to the faucets.

Since the second-floor supply lines tap into the first-floor lines, calculate the distance from your first-floor faucets to each faucet on the second floor. Repeat if you are planning on three floors—determine the distance from the second-floor faucet to the third floor. Add *all* the measurements together and multiply by 2 since you require one cold supply pipe and one hot. Additional 3/4-inch copper piping will be required to run to washing machines, outdoors and any special projects. Increase your totals by approximately 20% (multiply by 1.2) to allow for extras.

Optional plumbing materials that are small in quantity and price are explained, but not included in the calculations below. Flexi-hoses attach to the copper supply pipes from the wall to your faucet. For every faucet in your house, budget 2 hoses, typically 12 inches long, 2 nuts to attach the copper pipe and flexi-hoses together, 2 end caps to cover the hole in your wall and 2 copper "Ts."

For drain lines, 2-inch ABS/PVC pipes (refer to your architectural plans or local building codes to determine pipe material and size) run from the drain and connect to one main 3-inch ABS/PVC cleanout line. Measure the horizontal distance from every drain on each floor to the main horizontal 3-inch cleanout. The main horizontal line serves two purposes— venting up odors to the roof and running dirty water underground to a 3-inch PVC line that carries the water to the street sewers.

Calculate your 2-inch ABS/PVC piping (toilets may require 3-inch) needs by measuring the distance of each of your drains to the main vent/main 3-inch ABS/PVC cleanout. Don't forget the basement drain located under your concrete floor. For the main cleanout, measure the distance from your roof to the basement.

ABS/PVC "Ts" and "Js" are used to connect ABS/PVC straight drain lines. Plan on one "T" and one "J" per drain.

A 3-inch PVC drain line that runs underground from your house to the street sewer needs to be included. Measure the distance from your house to the end of your driveway.

If you are renovating, the quantity of plumbing materials required is surprisingly small. For example, if you are renovating your first floor kitchen, the amount of 3/4-inch copper piping required is simply the height distance from the existing copper pipe that runs along the basement ceiling to the new faucet. Multiply by 2 for hot and cold lines. Your calculations may come to only 10 feet! For ABS/PVC drain lines, measure the distance from the faucet to your main vent/cleanout; include clamps and connectors with a couple of flexi-hoses and you've pretty much covered it. For those of you with small renovations, ask for an itemized materials list from your plumber.

## ■ PLUMBING MATERIALS

| | | |
|---|---:|---:|
| 3/4-inch copper piping [(59ft. + 8ft.) × 2 + (14ft. + 34ft. + 20ft.) × 2] × 1.2 | 324 | |
| Average cost per foot ($1 × 270) | | $324 |
| 2-inch ABS/PVC drain pipes feet | 194 | |
| Average cost per foot ($0.80 per ft. × 194) | | $155 |
| 2 in. ABS/PVC Ts | 6 | |
| Average cost each ($4 × 6) | | $24 |
| 2 in. ABS/PVC Js | 6 | |
| Average cost each ($2.50 × 6) | | $15 |
| 3 in. ABS/PVC main cleanout, toilets plus line to city sewer | 190 | |
| Average cost per ft. ($1.30 × 130) | | $247 |
| Total Average Plumbing Materials Costs (excluding hot water tank and meter) | | $765 |

# ELECTRICAL

For new homes, major structural materials include the breaker panel, wires and receptacles. Nothing fancy or sexy here. If you are on a new lot and require electrical hookup from the street lines to your house, call your local electrical utility company to determine next steps. Local regulations may require the utility company to install the lines and meters. On the other hand, your contractor's certified electrician may be allowed to do the installation. If your contractor provides you with an estimate, consult a local building supply center for quantity and pricing. Or, Home Depot has devoted half an electrical aisle to illustrate what materials go where for your local area. You will find about five *major* materials costing under $100. Check your contractor's cost of materials and labor versus the electrical company's.

For the interior of your new home, budget for one 200-amp breaker panel. If renovating, check to see if you have sufficient breakers to accommodate additional appliances within your existing panel.

Connections from the panel to all your receptacles and fixtures are made with standard 14.2/14.3 gauge wire (refer to the architectural plans and local electrical codes). Large quantities of this popular standard wire are usually required and can be purchased in a variety of bolt sizes. The example below uses a 492-foot bolt. For a detailed wire measurement, count the number of receptacles and ceiling light fixtures in each room. Measure and add the distance in feet from your breaker panel to each fixture and receptacle. Divide your total by 492 feet to determine the number of 14.2/14.3 gauge wire required.

For a quicker, rougher estimate (illustrated below) allow for ten 14.2/14.3 standard wires to run from the breaker panel to the other end of the basement, back across again on each floor and from the top-floor ceiling back down to the basement breaker panel.

1. Determine the distance in feet from the basement panel to the opposite end of the basement, multiply by 10 and by the number of floors and include the top-storey ceiling as a floor.
2. Add the height from the basement ceiling to the top-floor ceiling and multiply this number by 10.
3. Add #1 and #2.

A heavier and more expensive wire, such as 8.3 and 10.3, is required for ovens, dryers and air conditioners. However, most appliances requiring a heavier gauge are located not far from the breaker panel. You can measure the distances individually and gain a fairly accurate estimate. Remember that electrical wires run from the panel up to, and along, the basement ceiling and back down to basement appliances.

The quantity and cost of the remainder of your structural materials are very small, including such items as metal fasteners to hold up the drywall to a stud or metal faceplates drilled onto studs when a wire is located directly behind it. Outlets require metal boxes that sit in the drywall—receptacles for attaching the wires and faceplates.

Also, two or three standard inexpensive light housing fixtures are usually required for the basement and garage. Other items include outdoor receptacles with gray plastic protection covers, larger receptacles for heavy duty items such as the oven, dryer and air conditioner. Most of the above items cost from between $2 and $5 each.

Cable wire for TVs and computers are covered in this electrical section and usually travel from close to the breaker panel, up, along and through the basement ceiling to desired locations. Measure the distance in feet.

For the installation of telephone wire, measure the distance, in feet, from the breaker panel to all the phone jacks. Record the number of jacks required.

### ■ NUMBER OF 14.2 GAUGE BOLTS

| | | |
|---|---|---|
| 14.2 wire $\{[(59 \times 10) \times 3] + (20 \times 10)\} = (1,970 \div 492)$ | 4 | |
| Average cost per bolt ($50 × 4) | | $200 |

### ■ NUMBER OF FEET OF 8.3 AND 10.3 GAUGE

| | | |
|---|---|---|
| 8.3 gauge | 18 | |
| Average cost per ft. ($1.50 per ft. × 18) | | $27 |
| 10.3 gauge | 25 | |
| Average cost per ft. ($2.80 × 25) | | $70 |

### ■ MISCELLANEOUS ELECTRICAL

| | | |
|---|---|---|
| 200-amp breaker panel average cost | | $200 |
| Cable wire for TV/computer (ft.) | 70 | |
| Average cost per ft. ($0.18 × 70) | | $13 |
| Telephone wire (ft.) | 100 | |
| Average cost per ft. ($0.25 × 100) | | $25 |
| Telephone jacks (ft.) | 6 | |
| Average cost each ($7.50 × 6) | | $42 |
| Outlets: receptacles, covers and boxes | 55 | |
| Average cost each ($3.00 × 55) | | $165 |
| Total Electrical Structural Materials (excluding materials to connect from street to house) | | $742 |

# Appendix 3
## Sample Finishing Materials Worksheet

Following is a sample illustration of a worksheet on which to record your selections. You should consider completing your own materials worksheet following the format below and staple it to a duo-folder. Once completed, ensure you give a copy to your contractor for reference.

| FINISHING | MATERIALS | STORE | BRAND | TOTAL $ |
|---|---|---|---|---|
| Windows | | | | |
| Window casings | | | | |
| Floor trim | | | | |
| Interior door—trim | | | | |
| Interior doors | | | | |
|    handles | | | | |
| Exterior door—front | | | | |
|    side | | | | |
|    handles | | | | |
| Sliding/French doors | | | | |
| Garage door | | | | |
| Garage door opener | | | | |
| | | | | |

| FINISHING | MATERIALS | STORE | BRAND | TOTAL $ |
|---|---|---|---|---|
| Shingles | | | | |
| Stucco | | | | |
| Stone | | | | |
| Brick | | | | |
| Siding | | | | |
| House trim | | | | |
| Shutters | | | | |
| Pillars | | | | |
| Eves | | | | |
| Soffits | | | | |
| Fascia | | | | |
| Driveway material | | | | |
| Furnace | | | | |
| Security system | | | | |
| Hot water tank | | | | |
| KITCHEN | | | | |
| Floor | | | | |
| LAUNDRY ROOM | | | | |
| Sinks | | | | |
| Faucets | | | | |
| Paint | | | | |

# Resources and Recommended Reading

**Websites:**

American Institute of Architects, www.ala.org

Better Business Bureau, www.bbb.org

Building-cost, www.building-cost.net

Build-smarter, www.build-smarter.com

Canadian Home Builders' Association, www.chba.ca

Craftsman Book Company, www.craftsman-book.com

Get-a-Quote, www.get-a-quote.net

Home Depot Commercial Direct Division and CD, *ProBook*

Home Planners, www.eplans.com

National Association of Homebuilders, www.nahb.org

Renovation Management Company, www.renomanagement.com

## Books, Magazines and Trade Publications

Better Homes and Gardens. *Basements: Your Guide to Planning and Remodelling*. Meredith Corp., 1999.

Better Homes and Gardens. *Home Plans Magazine*. Meredith Corp., 2004 series.

BNI Building News. *BNI Construction Dictionary Pocket Edition*. BNI Publications, 1997.

Ching, Francis, and Cassandra Adams. *Building Construction Illustrated*, 3rd Edition. Wiley Publishing, 2000.

Fine Homebuilding. *Foundations and Concrete Work*. Taunton Press, 2003.

Foot, David. *Boom, Bust and Echo: How to Profit from the Coming Demographic Shift*. Saint Anthony Messenger Press and Franciscan, 1997.

Home Depot. *Home Depot Home Improvement 1-2-3*. Meredith Corp., 2004.

Irwin, Robert. *Home Renovation Checklist*. McGraw-Hill, 2003.

Johnston, Amy. *What the Experts May Not Tell You About...Building or Renovating a Home*. Time Warner Group, 2004.

Koones, Sheri. *From Sand Castles to Dream House*. Hanley-Wood, 2002.

Lemos, Jain. *Home Renovation Workbook: A Step-by-Step Planner for Creating the Home of Your Dreams*. Chronicle Books, 2001.

Levy, Sidney M. *Project Management in Construction*, 4th Edition. McGraw-Hill, 2002.

Ogershok, Dave, and Richard Pray. *National Cost Estimator*. Craftsman Book Co., 2005.

Ortho Books. *Basements, Attics, and Bonus Rooms*. Meredith Corp., 2002.

Plesset, Dianne. *The Survival Guide: Home Remodelling*. D.P. Design Publishing, 2003.

Schwartz, Max. *Basic Concrete and Engineering for Builders*. Craftsman Book Co., 2000.

# Index

ABS, 62, 85, 87
air conditioning, 81, 87–89
angle boot, 159, 160
appliances, 82, 163
architect, 14–16, 75, 82, 101
    fees, 15
    *See also* plans
asphalt, 149–150
asphalt coating, 66, 153
attic, 77–80, 109

backer boards, 155
basement, 59–71
    ceiling, 69–70
    floor, 59–64, 105, 110, 115–116,
        150–151
    insulation, 60, 64, 68, 86
    stairs, 70–71
    walls, 64–68, 104–105, 110,
        151
    windows, 65–66, 68
Better Business Bureau, 19
block wall, 64
blueprints, 16, 101

Blue Stuff, 66
bonus payments, 141–142
breaker panel, 80–82, 162
brick, 74
budget, 17–18
building codes, 12, 73
    and basement, 60, 62, 64, 70
    and concrete, 104
    electrical, 82, 83, 162
    foundation, 105
    and lumber, 102
    plumbing, 85, 86
building inspection, 80, 131
building permits, 14, 16, 131

cable wires, 164
cast iron pipes, 85, 86
caulking, 91, 156
cement, 63, 151, *See also* concrete
cement boards, 155
change control process, 17, 38, 39,
    132, 142
cinder blocks, 64, 105, 120,
    151–152

collar ties, 77, 113
concrete, 63, 64,
    estimate, 104–105
    wall, 65, 105
construction, *See* individual materials
    and storeys
construction consultant, 94–95
contract, 18, 31, 45, 121
    changes, 17, 38, 39, 132, 142
    checklist, 131–132
contractor
    changing, 134
    dishonest, 37, 40–43, 47
    evaluating, 19–21
    large, 29–31
    mid-sized, 26–29
    small, 25–26, 30–31
"contractor speak," 5, 6, 11
cooling system, 88
copper pipe, 85, 86, 160–162
corner strips, 154
cost-plus method, 26–27
crawl space, 59
crossbar bridges, 148

daily log, 39
demolition, 122
design preparation, 14–17
disputes, 14, 132, 134
draftsperson, 14, 15–16
drainage systems, 118
    inside, 61–62, 152
    outside, 153
drain pipes, 62, 85–87, 160–162
drain screen, 66
drawings, 14–16, 69
drip edge, 79, 158
driveway, 118, 149
Drycore, 64, 106, 149
drywall, 68, 70, 73, 79, 89, 116–117
    compound, 154
    screws, 155
    tape, 154
ductwork, 69, 73, 88–89, 158–160

electrical, 68, 73, 79, 80–83
    materials, 162–164
equipment rental, 123
estimate
    35,000 sq. ft. home, 123, 126–128
    average, 18
    evaluation, 17–18, 24, 30
    format, 126
    labour, 25–43
    notations, 126–127
    your own, 24, 52, 99, 126–128
eves, 80, 118
exterior finishing, 74–75, 153
    basement walls, 66
    first storey wall, 73–74

fascia, 80
finishing materials, 45, 120–121
    costs, 97–98
    sample worksheet, 165–166
fireboard, 155
fire breaks, 68, 73

fireplace, 89–90
first storey, 69, 71–75
    ceiling, 75
    walls, 73–75
    windows and doors, 73, 74
flashing, 79, 156, 157
floor finishes, 63–64, 71–72, 119, 155
floor joists, 69, 103, 111, 112
footings, 59–60, 65, 105, 118, 151
foundation, 59–71, 105, 118
front entrance, 108, 109, 116, 155
furnace, 87–89, 158–159

garage, 105, 108, 118, 120, 150–151
grading, 70
gravel, 70, 118–119, 149

halogen lights, 83
headers, 111, 112
hot water tank, 86
house wrap, 74, 156

insulating concrete forms (ICFs), 64, 65
insulation, 109–110
    basement, 60, 64, 68, 86
    coverage, 147
    estimate, 110
    first storey, 73, 74, 75
    tubes, 157
    window, 91
interest rates, 145–146
invoices, 19, 48, 85, 132
    dishonest, 51–55, 93
    and estimates, 4, 6, 24, 31, 47
    final, 4, 6, 31, 35, 52, 142
    *See also* markups

jack posts, 60, 69, 152

kickbacks, 34–35, 41, 94
    manufacturer, 49
    supplier, 48–49

labour estimates, 25–43, 121–122
    fixed rate, 36–38
    hourly or variable, 38–40, 41, 42
liens, 132
lowballing, 17, 93, 99, 128
lumber costs, 96–97
    estimate, 102–104, 106–107
    and plans, 111, 112
    take-off, 98–99

management
    fee, 25–31, 34, 41, 42, 50–51
    responsibilities, 17
    styles, 9–12
markups, 31, 35, 45–48, 125, 128, 132
    standard, 48–49
    suspicious, 50–55
materials
    bill of, 17
    overcharges, 52–53
    worksheet, 165–166
    *See also* finishing materials;
        structural materials
measurements, 101–102, 108
meeting, 15, 21, 125, 132
    follow-up, 21–22
    preparation, 11, 13
    schedule, 39
model home prototype, 37–38
moisture proofing, 60–64
mortar, 64, 72, 151–152
mudsill, 69

National Association of Home Builders,
    19
National Estimator Service, 121
negotiating, 27, 34–35, 41–42
    estimates, 17–18, 30, 45
    tips, 134–143

outdoor receptacles, 163
outriggers, 77–78, 115

overcharges, 6, 52–53
overhead expenses, 27

paint and primer, 117
parging, 66, 151–152
payment schedule, 140–142
penalties, 141–142
per-square-foot rate, 33–34
plans, 12, 70, 77, 79, 99, 107,
    162
    preparation, 14–16
plastic sheathing, *See* vapor barrier
Platon membrane, 153
plumbing, 68, 69, 73, 79
    installation, 83–87
    materials, 160–162
plywood, 106–109
    underlayment, 119
polyethylene, 150
polystyrene, 60, 75, 110, 156
preparation, 13–22
project management fee, *See* management fee
project manager, 29
project schedule, 58, 140
PVC, 62, 85, 87, 152, 153

quotes, *See* estimates

rafters, 77, 112–113
rebar, 60, 63, 64, 65, 151
red tape, 74, 156
references, 19–20
registers, 159, 160
ridge board, 77, 112, 113
ridge vent, 157
risers, 70–71
roof, 75–80, 113–114
    and attic, 77–80
    felt, 79, 157
    sheathing, 79, 107–109
    trusses, 76

round pipe, 158–159
R-value, 65, 67, 74, 109–110, 147

second storey, 75
service entrance panel (SEP), 80–82
sewer, 62, 85, 87
sheathing, 73–74, 79, 96, 97, 106–109
Sheetrock, *See* drywall
shingles, 79
siding, 74
sill plate, 68, 149
sleeper studs, 115–116
soffits, 80
specialized trades, *See* tradesperson
stack elbows, 160
stairs, 70–71, 106–107, 148–149
stone, 74
stringer, 70, 148–149
structural materials, 46
    costs, 96
    formulas, 104–120, 148–164
    invoices, 85
    top 10, 95–98, 123
    *See also* individual materials
stucco, 74
stud wall, 66–68, 73, 75, 96, 103
    cost, 116
    insulation, 109–110
    lumber, 114–116
subcontractor, 28,
    as tradesperson, 35
    estimates, 33–36, 38
    hiring, 131
    kickbacks, 41
    management fee, 34–35
subfloor, 106–109, 115, 119, 155
sump pump, 62

taxes, 53–54
telephone wires, 164
TJI, 69
tongue-and-groove, 64

top plate, 68
top 10 materials, 95–98, 123
tradesperson, 12, 26, 27–28, 35
    average rates, 32–33, 122
    estimates, 31–33, 38, 43
    unqualified, 40
transformers, 83
travel time, 41–42
treads, 70–71
Typar, 74, 156
Tyvec, 74

utility company, 80, 86, 89, 162

valley flashing, 157
vapor barrier, 60, 64, 71, 73, 74, 75, 150
vents, 79, 87, 89, 90
volume discounts, 49

warranties, 51, 132
wastage, 103
water line, 86
weeping tile, 62, 153
windows, 97, 111, 112
    flashing, 156–157
    installation, 90–91
    *See also* basement; first storey
window wells, 66, 153
wire mesh, 150–151
wires, 80, 82, 162–164
wiring, *See* electrical
wood frame, 28, 57, 60, 65–66, 69, 98
    and fireplace, 89–90
    *See also* stud wall